WE LOVE HOLIDAYS!

THROUGH-THE-YEAR AND ACROSS-THE-CURRICULUM ACTIVITIES

GRADES 1-2

Hello! Press

Credits
Written by Cindy Barden with additional material by Becky J. Radtke
Layout/Design: Hello! Press
Inside Illustrations: Nancee Jean McClure and Becky J. Radtke
Cover Design: Hello! Press

ISBN: 0-9742916-2-5

TABLE OF CONTENTS

JANUARY

FEBRUARY

MARCH

APRIL

MAY

JUNE

JULY/AUGUST

WELCOME

Welcome to *We Love Holidays!*, one of four books in a series of across-the-curriculum activities for children from pre-kindergarten through grade 6. This book includes a wide variety of individual, small group, and circle time activities for first and second graders from art to zoology providing a valuable resource for parents, teachers, and homeschoolers.

The book is divided into eleven monthly sections— one for each month from September through June and a combined July/August unit. Each unit begins with a parent/teacher page with suggestions for additional activities related to that month; pre-activities to use before reproducibles with the same title; directions for specific reproducibles; activity extensions to use following reproducibles with the same title; and useful suggestions for parents and teachers.

Each unit includes holiday and seasonal activities suitable for first and second grade students designed to match their interests, knowledge, understanding, and abilities. Select those most appropriate to the skill level of your students.

This book offers opportunities and challenges to learn and reinforce basic skills, as well as more advanced material for those eager for more challenges as you recognize and respond to student diversity.

The across-the-curriculum material addresses the national standards and is suitable for parents or teachers to use at home or in school as a supplement to the classroom curriculum to teach, reinforce, and review vital, basic skills. Helping children build a strong foundation of skills and an eagerness to learn is a gift we can provide that will last a lifetime.

Activities cover a wide range of topics and include arts and crafts, language arts, math, science, and social studies. Specific skills addressed for each reproducible activity are listed at the top of the page and in the table of contents.

As a parent or teacher, you have a great influence on what students learn and their attitude towards learning. Your sense of fun and adventure will be contagious.

Meeting the Standards

Many web sites provide in-depth information about national educational standards and expectations. A plethora of information can be found using a search engine such as *www.looksmart.com* or *www.yahoo.com*. To locate standards, skills, and grade-appropriate expectations for a specific subject area, type in the subject name and the word standards.

You'll find a partial list of skills addressed in this book on the next page.

DEVELOPING SKILLS
AND MEETING THE STANDARDS WITH
WE LOVE HOLIDAYS!

Language Arts and Phonics Skills

- Initial consonant sounds
- Long and short vowel sounds
- Writing simple words and sentences
- Compound words
- Reading for details
- Journaling
- Creative and comparative writing
- Alliteration
- Antonyms
- Nouns
- Alphabetizing
- Rhyming

Math Skills

- Number sense and operations
- Sequencing and writing numbers
- Visual discrimination
- Problem solving: Addition and subtraction
- Geometry: Identifying shapes
- Creating equal sets
- Fractions as parts of a whole
- Counting, adding, and subtracting money
- Graphing
- Algebra
- Decoding
- Telling time
- Calendar skills
- Skip counting
- Using a grid

Science Skills

- Naming and classifying animals
- Recognizing the needs of plants
- Nutrition and health
- Weather and its effects on our lives
- Seasonal changes
- Environmental awareness
- Characteristics of natural objects

Social Studies Skills

- Self-awareness
- Friendship
- Family
- Holiday celebrations
- Getting along with others
- Cooperation and sharing
- Safety/Following rules
- Mapping skills
- Holiday symbols
- Patriotic symbols
- Community workers
- Citizenship
- History

Arts and crafts skills

- Scissors skills
- Coloring and drawing with various mediums
- Creating greeting cards and gifts
- Recognizing missing elements of a picture

Miscellaneous, Across-the-Curriculum Skills

- Critical/Creative thinking
- Following directions
- Making connections
- Logical reasoning
- Predicting
- Comparing and contrasting
- Using a Venn diagram

SEPTEMBER

Bert, the Bus Driver (Answers)

In order: Anderson, Cook, Dell, Franklin, Hernandez, Mason, Radke, Thomas, Woo, Zins

School Supplies (Answers)

pencil, crayons, eraser, ruler, scissors, notebook, markers, folder

Labor Day (Activity Extension)

Ask children to name other jobs people do and the tools they use to do their jobs. It may be easy for children to realize that a hammer and a shovel are tools, but more difficult for them to realize that a stapler, pencil, and textbook are also tools.

People at Work (Activity Extension)

Explain that Labor Day is a holiday to honor workers. Talk about different jobs people do. Ask children to name the occupations shown on the activity page and explain what each one does, what tools they use, and how they help us.

Leftover Leaves (Activity Extension)

Give each child a plastic, reclosable sandwich bag and take them on a nature hike to a park or woods. Encourage them to collect a variety of fallen leaves, nuts, pinecones, acorns, and other nature items. When you return to the classroom, students can combine what they collected, then sort and classify the items.

Pressed leaves and other fall objects make great classroom decorations. Students can use them for graphing activities, as well as arts and crafts projects.

Apple Addition (Activity Extension)

Celebrate fall with a trip to an apple orchard. Provide several types of apples (McIntosh, Delicious, Granny, etc.) for children to share at snack time. Let them taste and compare different varieties.

Back to School–Safely (Activity Extension)

Let children take turns reading the safety rules they wrote. Ask children for other rules that would be appropriate. For example: Always sit on the school bus. Talk quietly so you don't distract the bus driver.

Talk about the reasons for safety rules and how they help us. Whenever possible, word the rule in a positive way, rather than negative: Look both ways before crossing the street. Always wear a bike helmet when riding your bike.

National Anthem Day (Activity)

While held captive on a British warship bombarding Fort McHenry on September 14, 1814, Francis Scott Key wrote the famous words we know as "The Star-Spangled Banner." It officially became the U.S. national anthem in 1931. Celebrate the anniversary of this event by singing our national anthem with the class.

Celebrate Grandparents' Day (Activity Extension)

National Grandparents' Day is the Sunday after Labor Day.

Read *Just Grandma and Me* and *Just Grandpa and Me* by Mercer Mayer to the children. Children can compare their grandparents to Little Critter's.

Ask children to tell the group about their favorite grandparent. If a child has no grandparents, ask him or her to talk about a older relative, family friend, or neighbor.

Positive Posters (Activity Extension)

Let children work together in small groups to create Back to School Safety posters. As a group, ask them to think of a good safety rule and write it on the poster. They can decorate the posters with paint, glitter glue, illustrations cut from magazine or downloaded from the Internet. Display posters in the school library, cafeteria, or hallway near your classroom.

Bert, the Bus Driver

Bert is busy planning his bus route for the first day of school. He decided to make his stops in ABC order. The name of each family is written on the roof of their home. Help Bert by numbering them from 1 to 10 in alphabetical order.

Woo

Cook

Radke

Mason

Thomas

Hernandez

Dell

Anderson

Zins

Franklin

Reproducible
HP101

Beat the Bell

The school bell will ring soon! Help Juan, Min, and Jane find their way to class as quickly as you can. Don't forget to pick up their backpacks along the way!

START

HP101

School Supplies

Use the vowels to fill in the blanks to complete the list of what you need for school. The picture clues can help you!

a e i o u

p _ n c _ l

cr _ y _ n s

_ r _ s _ r

r _ l _ r

sc _ ss _ rs

n _ t _ b _ _ k

m _ r k _ rs

f _ l d _ r

Labor Day

Labor Day is a holiday to honor workers. Think about different jobs people do and what tools they use to do their jobs.

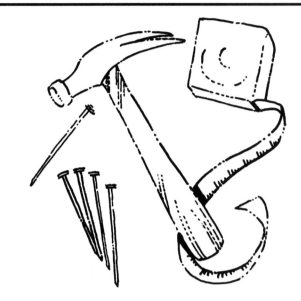

Who would use these tools?

_____

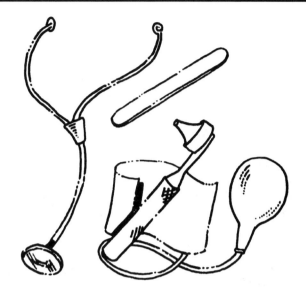

Who would use these tools?

_____

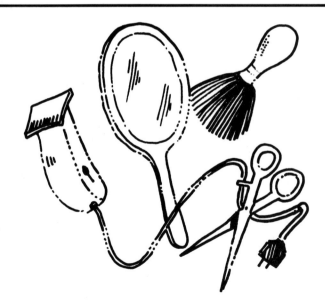

Who would use these tools?

_____

Who would use these tools?

_____

Social Studies: Self-Esteem/Predicting

People at Work

Labor Day is a holiday to honor workers.

Draw a picture of yourself doing a job when you grow up.

HP101

Math: Counting/Science: Classifying

Leftover Leaves

Jake and Jan raked the yard, but they missed so many leaves! Count the number of each kind of leaf and write the numbers by the pictures at the bottom.

Apple Addition

There's nothing like an autumn trip to the apple orchard! But there's more here to do than buy fruit. Solve the addition equation in each basket. Then color the apple beside it that shows the correct sum.

1. $1 + 5 =$ 4   6

2. $3 + 4 =$ 7   2

3. $2 + 2 =$ 1   8   4   5

4. $5 + 3 =$ 9   8

5. $9 + 0 =$ 7   9

6. $8 + 2 =$ 6   10   7   4   9

HP101

Name _____ Date _____

Back to School—Safely

For each picture, write a safety rule.

1. _____
_____
_____
_____

2. _____
_____
_____
_____

3. _____
_____
_____
_____

4. _____
_____
_____
_____

Reproducible HP101

Guessing Grandparents

Tyler stopped at his grandparents' home with an important message for them. Use the code to write the words on the blanks.

Social Studies: Family/Language Arts: Creative Writing

Celebrate Grandparents' Day

Write words to describe your grandparents.

_____   _____   _____

_____   _____   _____

_____   _____   _____

_____   _____   _____

List things you like to do with your grandparents.

_____

_____

_____

_____

_____

Write a short story or poem about you and your grandparents.

_____

_____

_____

_____

_____

_____

_____

_____

_____

_____

_____

When you finish, use your best printing and write your story or poem on fancy paper. Add a picture. Give it to your grandparents.

OCTOBER

Apples (Solution)

R	E	R	E	D	D	E	J
A	G	O	O	D	O	T	U
F	R	U	I	T	O	P	I
H	O	N	T	E	A	T	C
E	W	D	A	P	P	L	E
A	N	D	G	I	C	C	T
L	S	N	A	C	K	I	P
T	O	E	S	K	R	D	I
H	Y	K	T	T	R	E	E
Y	U	M	M	Y	P	R	S

October Is a Yummy Month (Fun Fact)

Did you know that October has been set aside to honor three of our favorite foods? October is National Pasta Month, National Pizza Month, and National Popcorn Poppin' Month. Celebrate with a class party—or two or three!

Columbus Day Game (Activity)

Conclude a unit on Columbus and his voyage to the New World with this game students can design and play. Divide children into groups of four to six to make the game boards. (You may want to make one in advance as a model.) Encourage children to write additional game cards related to what they learned about Columbus and his voyage of exploration.

Pizza Math (Answers)

1. 6; 2. 8; 3. 5; 4. 9; 5. $\frac{1}{3}$; 6. $\frac{2}{4}$ or $\frac{1}{2}$; 7. $\frac{1}{6}$; 8. $\frac{6}{8}$ or $\frac{3}{4}$; 9. $\frac{2}{6}$ or $\frac{1}{3}$; 10. $\frac{3}{8}$; 11. $\frac{5}{8}$; 12. $\frac{1}{8}$

A Tangled Tongue Twister (Answer)

Peter Pumpkin put a patch on Pat's purple pajama pants.

A Tangled Tongue Twister (Activity Extension)

Encourage students to make up other alliterative sentences and share them with the group.

EEK! (Answers)

1. creek
2. Greek
3. sleek
4. hide and seek
5. peek-a-boo
6. meek
7. cheek
8. week
9. reek
10. seek
11. book
12. booties
13. caboose
14. baboon
15. boot

EEK! (Activity Extension)

More advanced students may be able to complete this activity on their own. This activity would be best done by a group.

Give children other words and let them add letters to make new words. Suggestions: *and, ant, ink, ear, ore, am.*

Halloween Party (Game)

Cut a large pumpkin shape from orange construction paper. Decorate with eyes and mouth. Cut a nose from black construction paper. Blindfold and spin a child, then have him or her try to pin the nose on the jack-o'-lantern.

Name _____   Date _____

Apples

Look up and down to find the apple words hidden in the puzzle.

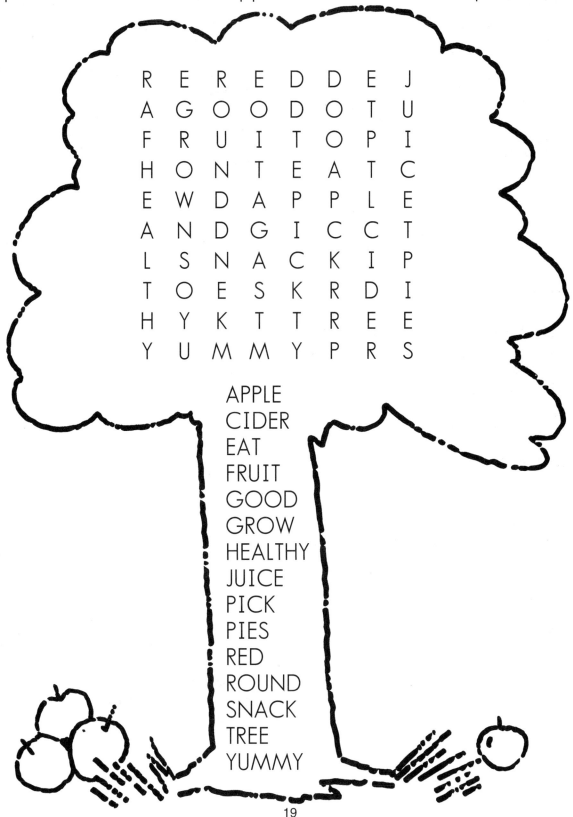

```
R   R   E   R   E   D   D   E   J
A   G   O   O   D   O   T   U
F   R   U   I   T   O   P   I
H   O   N   T   E   A   T   C
E   W   D   A   P   P   L   E
A   N   D   G   I   C   C   T
L   S   N   A   C   K   I   P
T   O   E   S   K   R   D   I
H   Y   K   T   T   R   E   E
Y   U   M   M   Y   P   R   S
```

APPLE
CIDER
EAT
FRUIT
GOOD
GROW
HEALTHY
JUICE
PICK
PIES
RED
ROUND
SNACK
TREE
YUMMY

HP101

Columbus Day Game

Work as a group to make a Columbus game board. Use a large sheet of paper. Color it blue for the ocean. Decorate the ocean with fish, coral, whales, and other sea creatures.

Draw a wiggly path across the ocean and divide it into spaces. Mark one end Spain and the other end the Bahamas.

Cut out the cards. Place them facedown in a pile.

Throw a die to see who goes first. Each player uses a game marker and starts at Spain. Take turns rolling the die and moving that number of spaces. If you roll a one, draw a card and follow the directions instead.

See who will be the first to reach the Bahamas.

Bad storm. Go back 3.	
Great day for sailing! Move ahead 2.	

Clear skies. Good wind. Move ahead 4.	Stop and watch the whales. Lose a turn.

You spotted land. Take an extra turn.	Fresh water is running low. Go back 3.	Everyone is happy today. Go ahead 5.	No wind today. Lose a turn while you wait for it to rise.
Good wind in the right direction. Move ahead 4.	Is that a mermaid up ahead? Move ahead 4 and take a look.	Detour around the giant squid. Go back 1.	The compass isn't working today. Go back 2.
Big catch of fresh fish. Take an extra turn.	No fish biting today. Go back 2.	Big waves today. Roll a 4 or 5 to move.	Dolphins bring good luck. Move ahead 3.
You're feeling a bit seasick. Lose a turn and get better.	Today is a holiday. Celebrate by moving ahead 5.	You lost your lucky horseshoe. Lose a turn while you look for it.	Let the breezes blow you ahead 3.

HP101

National Pizza Month

What if you could put anything you wanted on a pizza? Instead of tomato sauce would you use peanut butter? Jelly? Frosting?

What could replace the cheese: Coconut? Chow mein noodles?

How about toppings: Cherries? Peanuts? Cereal? Chocolate chips?

Design your own pizza. List the ingredients you used.

Ingredients:

_____

_____

_____

_____

_____

_____

_____

_____

_____

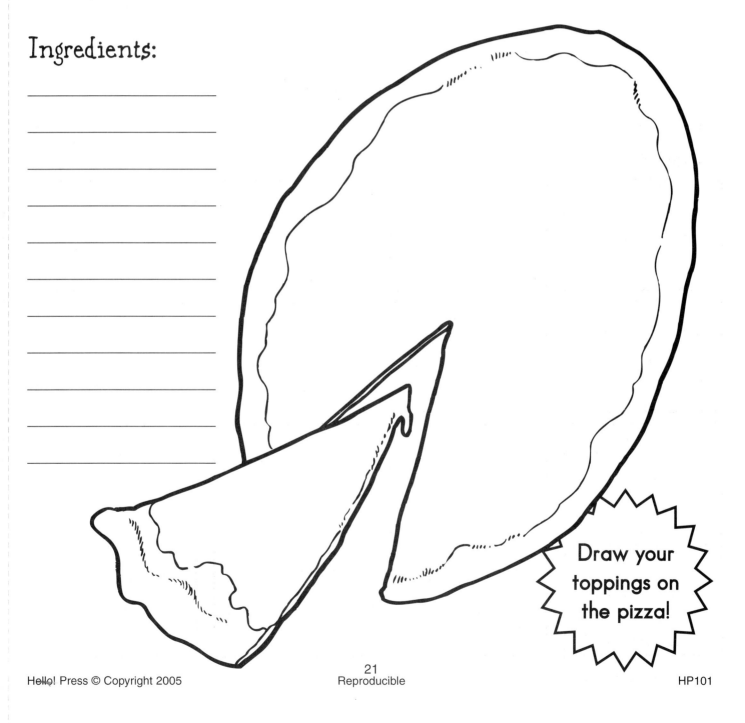

Draw your toppings on the pizza!

HP101

Pizza Math

October Is National Pizza Month!

Write the total number of slices below each pizza.

1. _____   2. _____   3. _____   4. _____

Write the fractions for the missing parts of the pizzas.

5.

_____

6.

_____

7.

_____

8.

_____

9.

_____

10.

_____

11.

_____

12.

_____

HP101

The Long and Short of It

Color the pictures of animals with long vowel sounds. Remember, a long vowel sound is one that says its own name. Write the name of each animal. Use the words in the box.

ant	dog	fish	frog	goat	pig	seal	snake	whale

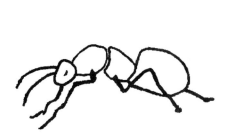  

_____

_____

_____   _____   _____

HP101

Name _____   Date _____

Halftime

Show the times on the clocks.

1. Devan and his grandpa left for the game at 1:00.

2. The football game started at 1:30.

3. The home teamed scored a touchdown at 1:45.

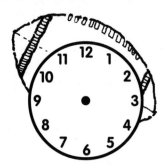

4. Halftime started at 2:30.

5. The game ended at 3:45.

6. They went home at 6:15.

HOME	VISITORS
14	3

HP101

Name _____ Date _____

A Tangled Tongue Twister

Watch the signs. Add or subtract. Use the code to write the tongue twisters.

A	C	E	H	I	J	K	L	M	N	O	P	R	S	T	U
10	13	15	3	8	18	4	11	7	17	6	14	5	16	12	9

$$7 \atop +7 \qquad 9 \atop +6 \qquad 5 \atop +7 \qquad 8 \atop +7 \qquad 2 \atop +3$$

Answer ___ ___ ___ ___ ___

Letter ___ ___ ___ ___ ___

$$9 \atop +5 \quad 6 \atop +3 \quad 4 \atop +3 \quad 10 \atop +4 \quad 2 \atop +2 \quad 6 \atop +2 \quad 8 \atop +9 \qquad 11 \atop +3 \quad 2 \atop +7 \quad 7 \atop +5$$

Answer ___ ___ ___ ___ ___ ___ ___   ___ ___ ___

Letter ___ ___ ___ ___ ___ ___ ___   ___ ___ ___

$$12 \atop -2 \qquad 18 \atop -4 \quad 17 \atop -7 \quad 15 \atop -3 \quad 14 \atop -1 \quad 10 \atop -7 \qquad 10 \atop -4 \quad 20 \atop -3$$

Answer ___   ___ ___ ___ ___ ___   ___ ___

Letter ___   ___ ___ ___ ___ ___   ___ ___

$$19 \atop -5 \quad 20 \atop -10 \quad 16 \atop -4 \quad 18 \atop -2 \qquad 20 \atop -6 \quad 11 \atop -2 \quad 9 \atop -4 \quad 18 \atop -4 \quad 17 \atop -6 \quad 18 \atop -3$$

Answer ___ ___ ___ ' ___   ___ ___ ___ ___ ___ ___

Letter ___ ___ ___   ___   ___ ___ ___ ___ ___ ___

$$6 \atop +8 \quad 5 \atop +5 \quad 12 \atop +6 \quad 2 \atop +8 \quad 4 \atop +3 \quad 7 \atop +3 \qquad 16 \atop -2 \quad 14 \atop -4 \quad 19 \atop -2 \quad 16 \atop -4 \quad 19 \atop -3$$

Answer ___ ___ ___ ___ ___ ___   ___ ___ ___ ___ ___

Letter ___ ___ ___ ___ ___ ___   ___ ___ ___ ___ ___

HP101

Name _____ Date _____

Scarecrow Goes Shopping

How much money does Scarecrow need for each item?

STRAW HAT **25¢**

How many nickels? _____

ROPE BELT **17¢**

How many nickels and pennies? _____ nickels and _____ pennies

BUTTON EYES
12¢

How many dimes and pennies? _____ dimes and _____ pennies

RAGGED JEANS WITH PATCHES **75¢**

How many quarters? _____

PLAID SHIRT WITH PATCHES **50¢**

How many dimes? _____

Name _____ Date _____

Purple Pumpkin Parts

October is the perfect time to pick pumpkins! Before you choose your favorite, take out your purple crayon. Then use it to color in the fraction area shown on each pumpkin stem.

　　　　　　　　　　HP101

Name _____ Date _____

Scary Harry

No one knows what Scary Harry looks like because he always wears a scary hairy costume. Today his costume is in the wash.

Color Scary Harry the way you think he looks without his costume.

HP101

EEK!

Each word below contains the word **eek**. Use the clues to fill in the missing letters to make new words.

1. A stream   ___ ___ e e k
2. A person from Greece   ___ ___ e e k
3. Very smooth   ___ ___ e e k
4. A game   h i d e a n d ___ e e k
5. A baby game   ___ e e k - a - b o o
6. Shy   ___ e e k
7. Part of your face   ___ ___ e e k
8. Seven days   ___ e e k
9. Stink   ___ e e k
10. Look for   ___ e e k

Boo!

Each word below contains the word **boo**. Use the clues to fill in the missing letters to make new words.

11. Something to read   b o o ___
12. What a baby wears
    on its feet   b o o ___ ___ ___ ___
13. The last car on a train   ___ ___ b o o ___ ___
14. A type of ape   ___ ___ b o o ___
15. What we wear on our
    feet in winter   b o o ___ ___

HP101

Celebrate Children's Book Week (Activity)

Since 1919, educators, librarians, booksellers, and families have celebrated Children's Book Week during the week before Thanksgiving. Celebrate the love of reading with storytelling, parties, author and illustrator appearances, and other book-related events.

In an Emergency (Activity Extension)

Talk with the children about each picture. Did everyone agree on which situations were emergencies and which weren't? Ask children to take turns explaining why they thought a situation was or was not an emergency. Ask them to give other examples of emergencies. Be sure to explain how to call for help in an emergency.

Children can use toy telephones or discarded real ones that no longer work to practice dialing 911. This is also a great opportunity to reinforce dialing their home telephone numbers.

Share a Thanksgiving Story

Suggested stories: *Don't Eat Too Much Turkey* by Miriam Cohen and *The First Thanksgiving* by Jean Craighead George.

Happy Thanksgiving (Answers)

3 harvest	4 gravy	5 pilgrims
5 turkey	5 potatoes	3 gobble
2 family	2 dessert	4 meal
1 dinner	1 cranberries	1 corn
4 pumpkin pie	3 friends	2 dressing

Use a search engine such as *www.yahoo.com* or *www.looksmart.com* and type in the key words *Book Week* to find a multitude of web sites featuring suggestions, activities, and lesson plans for celebrating National Book Week.

Happy Thanksgiving (Activity Extension)

After children complete this activity, ask them to share their reasons to be thankful with the class.

On the Farm (Answer)

A	C	A	T	Z	T	S	R	H	H	I
B	D	E	U	L	M	G	O	O	S	E
C	O	W	R	Y	Z	F	A	R	M	U
O	G	H	K	Z	F	R	G	S	E	M
R	S	H	E	E	S	H	E	E	P	Y
N	O	M	Y	R	I	R	Y	C	H	R
I	S	T	M	A	L	S	A	N	N	D
D	D	H	P	L	O	W	A	P	P	H
Y	N	E	I	W	H	G	R	R	Y	E
A	R	O	G	F	T	E	B	A	R	N

Plenty of Pie (Answers)

pumpkin; apple; cherry; blueberry

Turkey Time (Activity Extension)

After children complete the Turkey Time Math activity, they can make additional sets using blocks, plastic animals, toy cars, etc. Have them sort the toys into groups of 2, 3, 4, 5, 6, 7, 8, 9, or 10.

Use the sets to help children practice counting by 2s, 3s, 5s, and 10s.

What's for Dinner? (Activity)

Talk with children about special foods they enjoy during the holidays that they don't eat very often the rest of the year.

Math: Visual Discrimination

Book Week

These children are celebrating Book Week in November at the library. If you look closely, you'll find five things that are wrong. Circle them. Color the picture.

HP101

In an Emergency

Look at each picture. Is it an emergency? Should you dial 911?
Circle **Yes** or **No**.

Is this an emergency?

Yes   No

Is this an emergency?

Yes   No

Is this an emergency?

Yes   No

Is this an emergency?

Yes   No

Poetry in Motion

Write words that rhyme with the first word in each row.

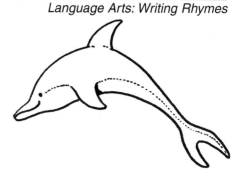

walk: _____

_____

glide: _____

_____

fly: _____

_____

run: _____

_____

jog: _____

_____

skip: _____

_____

hop: _____

_____

dance: _____

_____

float: _____

_____

On the back of this page, use your rhyming words to write a poem about motion.

Enjoy the Election

The second Tuesday of November is Election Day. It's when we choose people to represent our towns, state, and country! What an honor and privilege this is! Haley and Ty want to remind people to do something. Count how many times they've said, "Vote." Circle that number on their ballot.

HP101

Name _____ Date _____

Terry Turkey's Hiding Place

Read the story. Finish the story by drawing the ending. Color the pictures.

1. The day before Thanksgiving is not a good day—if you're a turkey.

2. Terry Turkey needed a good place to hide. He thought about hiding under the bed, but the dust made him sneeze.

3. He thought about hiding in the cupboard behind a can of cranberries. No, that would not be a good idea.

4. Then he had a great idea. He found the best hiding place of all. No one would find him until the day after Thanksgiving.

HP101

Name _____ Date _____

Happy Thanksgiving

Number each group of Thanksgiving words in ABC order.
Color the pictures.

_____ harvest

_____ turkey

_____ family

_____ dinner

_____ pumpkin pie

_____ gravy

_____ potatoes

_____ dessert

_____ cranberries

_____ friends

_____ pilgrims

_____ gobble

_____ meal

_____ corn

_____ dressing

List five things you are thankful for.

_____

_____

_____

_____

_____

HP101

On the Farm

Find and circle the word **turkey** and the other farm words in the puzzle.

```
A   C   A   T   Z   T   S   R   H   H   I
B   D   E   U   L   M   G   O   O   S   E
C   O   W   R   Y   Z   F   A   R   M   U
O   G   H   K   Z   F   R   G   S   E   M
R   S   H   E   E   S   H   E   E   P   Y
N   O   M   Y   R   I   R   Y   C   H   R
I   S   T   M   A   L   S   A   N   N   D
D   D   H   P   L   O   W   A   P   P   H
Y   N   E   I   W   H   G   R   R   Y   E
A   R   O   G   F   T   E   B   A   R   N
```

BARN	COW	GOOSE	PIG	SILO
CAT	DOG	HEN	PLOW	TURKEY
CORN	FARM	HORSE	SHEEP	

HP101

Name _____   Date _____

Turkey Tally

These turkey teams are having a Thanksgiving contest! Count the tail feathers on each bird and write the numbers on their signs. Then add the two numbers in each row and write the sum on the ribbons. The pair with the highest score wins! Color the winner's ribbon blue.

38
Reproducible

Name _____ Date _____

Plenty of Pie

Nothing tastes better after Thanksgiving dinner than a piece of pie! Look at each picture and write its first letter on the blank. When you're done you'll find four kinds of pie Grandma made!

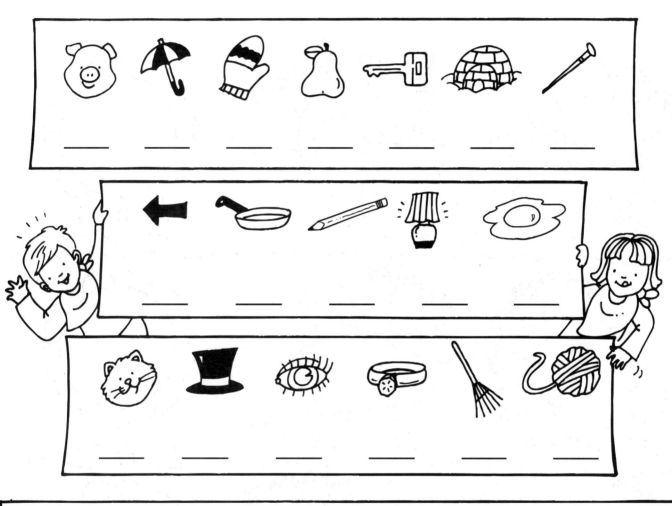

HP101

Name _____ Date _____

Turkey Time Math

Draw circles around the turkeys to make sets of 5. Then, color the turkeys.

How many sets of 5 did you make? _____

Count by 5s. How many turkeys in all? _____

DECEMBER

Happy Kwanzaa and Happy Hanukkah (Activity Extension)

If any of the children celebrate either of these two holidays at home, ask them to tell their classmates more about the holiday, why and how it is celebrated.

I Like Winter. Do You? (Activity)

Some words that can be made from the letters in *winter* are:

in	newt	tine	win
ire	nit	twin	wine
it	rent	twine	wire
net	tier	went	wit
new	tin	wet	wren

Cookie Cutter Art (Activity)

Provide a variety of shapes of cookie cutters. Let children trace the shapes on colored construction paper and cut them out to make holiday ornaments or gifts for family members. They can use markers, paints, and stickers to decorate their ornaments. Use a hole punch and hang decorations with colored yarn or ribbon.

Let It Snow, Let It Snow, Let It Snow! (Activity)

Help children cut snowflakes from white paper or tissue paper. Decorate the snowflakes with glitter glue. Use the snowflakes to decorate your room. Children can also give them as gifts to friends and relatives.

Hats for the Snowman (Activity)

Plan a Hat Day. Ask children to wear their favorite hats. Give prizes for funniest, longest, shortest, reddest, fuzziest, etc. Make sure you wear a hat, too!

Make Popcorn Balls (Activity)

Get into the holiday spirit by making popcorn balls with the children.
1. Make 5 quarts of popcorn.
2. Combine in a buttered saucepan:
   2 c. sugar   1½ c. water
   ½ tsp. salt   1 tsp. vinegar
   ½ c. light corn syrup
3. Cook over medium heat to a hard boil. Stir constantly with a wooden spoon.
4. Stir in 1 tsp. vanilla.
5. Pour mixture over popcorn, stirring slightly to mix.
6. Butter hands lightly. Shape into balls. (Mixture may be hot.)
7. Let children add gumdrop eyes, candy corn, raisins, or chocolate chips to make holiday faces.

Gift Giving (Activity)

Handmade gifts are special to both the giver and the recipient. Children can make up a short story or poem. Have them use their best printing on fancy paper and illustrate their work. To make the gift more special, help them frame the story or poem (or a special drawing or painting).

Parade of Lights (Activity)

Many winter holidays include lighting candles or colored lights. Have your own parade of lights. For safety, children can use flashlights instead of candles. Cover the flashlights with colored cellophane to produce many colors. Rather than a solemn procession, let students dance and sing as they go. They could carry colored crepe paper streamers and play percussion instruments.

Winter Words (Activity Extension)

As children make different sentences, remind them that all "real" sentences begin with a capital letter and end with either a period, question mark, or exclamation mark. Encourage them to make additional word cards. Children can take their favorite sentence, glue the words in order on a sheet of paper, and draw a picture to match.

Name _____ Date _____

Snow Words and Sun Words

Combine these words with **snow** to make new words. Write the new words.
Example: snow + ball = snowball

drift	fall	flake	fort	man
plow	shoes	storm	suit	

_____   _____

_____   _____

_____   _____

_____

Combine the words in the box with **sun** to make new words.
Write the new words.

Example: sun + bonnet = sunbonnet

flower	glasses	lamp	light	rise
screen	set	shine	spot	tan
bathe	beam	day	fish	

_____   _____   _____

_____   _____   _____

_____   _____   _____

_____   _____   _____

Winter, Summer, or Both?

Write each word where it belongs on the Venn diagram.

baseball	beach ball	boots	cold	fan
fun	games	hockey	hot	ice
lemonade	mittens	picnic	play	rain
read	sandals	school	sled	shorts
swimsuit	snow	sun	umbrella	

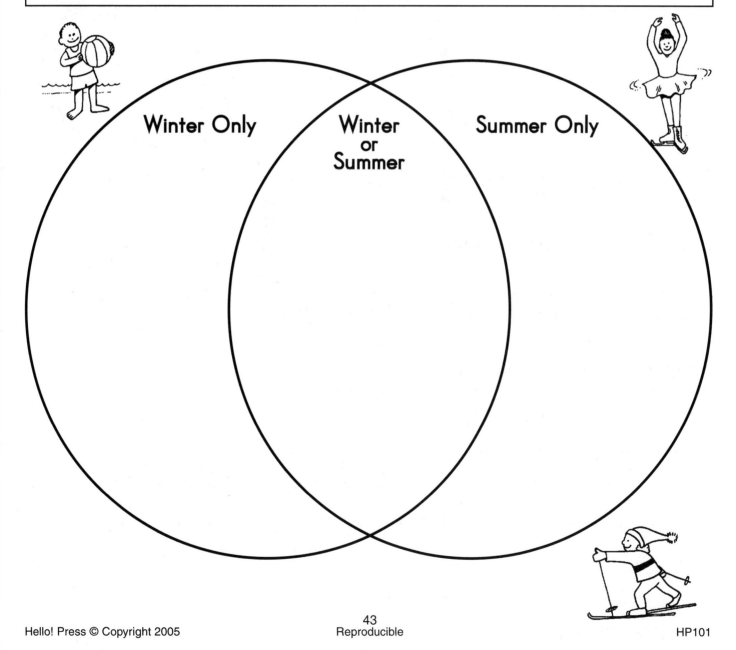

Winter Only   Winter or Summer   Summer Only

HP101

Happy Hanukkah

Teachers and Parents: Teach children to play this traditional Jewish dreidel game.

1. Each person puts the same number of items in the center of the table. Items can be candies, animal crackers, marbles, etc.

2. Players take turns spinning the dreidel. When the dreidel stops, this is what you do:

If the dreidel lands on take half the items.

If the dreidel lands on take nothing.

It the dreidel lands on put two more items in the middle.

If the dreidel lands on take all items from the middle.

(Either game ends or players put the same number of items in the center and continue.)

If you don't have a dreidel, make your own.

Cut the pattern on the following page from stiff paper or light cardboard. Fold and tape.

HP101

Dreidel Pattern

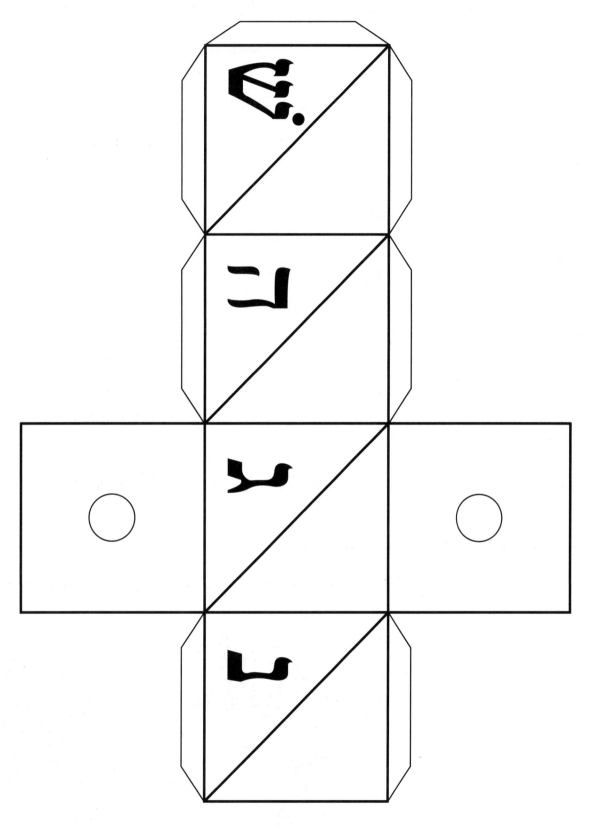

Reproducible HP101

Name ______________________________ Date ______________

Science: Winter/Language Arts: Comparative Writing

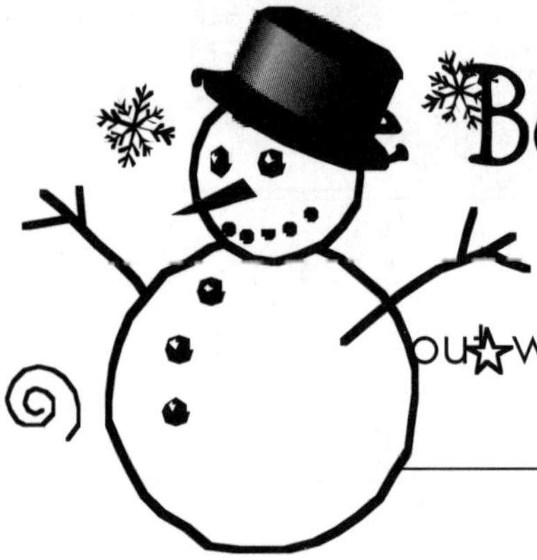

e Best and Worst of Winter

ou what you like most about winter.

Write about what you like least about winter.

Name _____ Date _____

I Like Winter. Do You?

A sentence that tells something ends in a period.

It is cold today⊙

A sentence that asks a question ends in a question mark.

Is it cold today⑦

Read the sentences. Write a period or question mark at the end of each sentence.

1. Jake likes to ice skate
2. Can you ice skate
3. Will it be cold today
4. I like cocoa
5. Kate is my sister
6. Do you have a sister
7. The snow is falling
8. Will you make a snowman
9. Can we ride on your sled
10. How many words can you make using the letters in the word **winter**? Write your words on the lines.

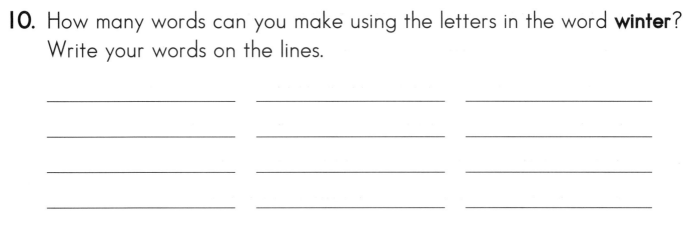

HP101

Presents to Pack

The elves have been busy packing gifts for Santa! Solve the subtraction equations on the gifts. Write the answers on the sacks.

$10 - 6 =$

$7 - 5 =$

$9 - 4 =$

$18 - 9 =$

$15 - 7 =$

$13 - 7 =$

$20 - 10 =$

$19 - 6 =$

HP101

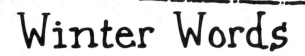

Winter Words

Fill in the chart with words that begin with
the letter at the beginning of each row.

	An animal	A place	Someone's name	Something to eat	Something to wear	A game or sport
W						
I						
N						
T						
E						
R						

HP101

Winter Sentences

Cut out the word cards. Arrange them to make fun winter sentences. If you need more words, make your own word cards.

snow	the	cold	am	snowman
ice	and	deep	have	build
she	be	on	made	saw
it	sled	the	sunny	wore
skate	day	but	large	had
went	coat	will	by	quickly
is	today	boy	a	fun
was	slide	I	and	small
build	go	hat	he	under
white	are	boots	girl	the
very	is	play	he	a
in	shove	goes	mittens	shoe

HP101

Happy Kwanzaa

Kwanzaa is a holiday celebrated by African-American families. The **kinara** is a candle holder with seven candles. Seven important ideas called principles are recited each day of the holiday. These remind people to work together. The holiday lasts for seven days. Even the word **Kwanzaa** has seven letters!

Seven is an important number in the celebration of Kwanzaa. How many ways can you add and subtract to equal 7? Fill in the equations.

_____ + _____ = 7   _____ − _____ = 7

_____ + _____ = 7   _____ − _____ = 7

_____ + _____ = 7   _____ − _____ = 7

_____ + _____ = 7   _____ − _____ = 7

_____ + _____ = 7   _____ − _____ = 7

_____ + _____ = 7   _____ − _____ = 7

HP101

New Year's Math (Activity)

Math stories get progressively more difficult. You may need to do some of them with the children. Encourage children to draw pictures or use manipulatives to help solve the problems.

New Year's Math (Activity Extension)

Make up story problems using dates for children to solve.

> Examples: *If Josh was born in 1989, how old would he be now?*
>
> *Trisha is 11 years old. What year was she born?*

Snowflake Math (Activity Extension)

Students can make and say number sentences using small toys like cars, blocks, or beads. This gives them a "hands-on" approach, as well as a visual one for simple math equations.

I Have a Dream (Pre-Activity)

Read a book about Martin Luther King, Jr. to the children. Discuss the words used in the puzzle.

Free at Last! The Story of Martin Luther King, Jr. by Angela Bull

Happy Birthday, Martin Luther King by Jean Marzollo

Martin Luther King Day by Linda Lowery

Snowflake Cutouts (Activity)

Let children cut snowflakes from basket-style coffee filters. Fold the filters in half, then in thirds before cutting. Children can glue strip magnets to the back to make refrigerator magnets.

I Have a Dream (Solution)

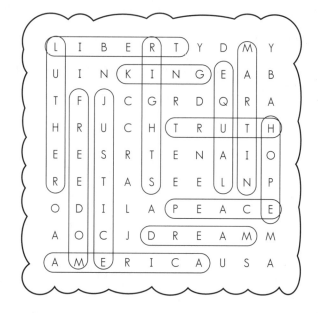

Different Colored Shirts Week (Activity)

Brighten up a winter week by asking children to wear a specific colored shirt, blouse, or sweater each day of the week. (You, too, of course.) Clothing could be solid colors or prints with that day's color. Those who do not have clothing that color could wear white.

Take a survey in class to see who likes which color the best. Write the color words on the board: *red, green, blue, yellow, purple,* and *pink.* Show children how to make tally marks for each vote, then add the tally marks for the total votes for each color. Children can make graphs to show the results of the survey. Homeschoolers can take a survey among friends and family members.

Building a Snowman (Activity)

Let children use modeling clay to make "mechanical" snowpeople. They can add nuts, bolts, or other small metal items for snowpeople details.

HP101

Name _____ Date _____

New Year's Eve

This bear family is celebrating New Year's Eve. Look carefully at the picture, then circle the answers to the questions. Write **Happy New Year** on the banner and color the picture.

1. What are they throwing?

confetti   leaves   mittens

2. How do they look?

sad   angry   happy

3. What treat will they eat?

pickles   cupcakes   bread

4. How many party hats do they have?

ten   six   three

HP101

Name _____ Date _____

New Year's Math

Write the equations and answers.

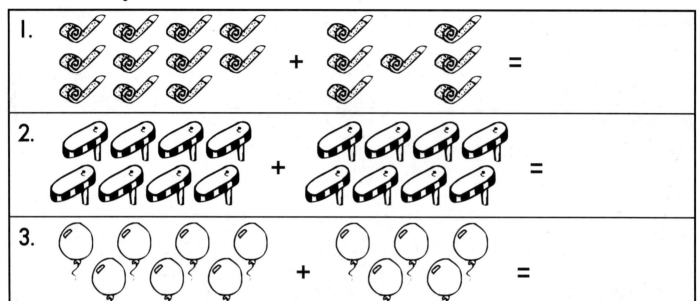

Write the answers.

4. Write the year: _____

5. What year will it be in 10 years? _____

6. How old will you be in the year 2020? _____

7. Twenty-eight people went to a New Year's party.
    Six left early. How many were still at the party? _____

8. Mario made 36 cupcakes for the New Year's party.
    There were 4 left after the party.
    How many cupcakes did people eat? _____

9. Hannah blew up 17 balloons for the party.
    Nine of them popped. How many were left? _____

10. Madeline made 22 blue party hats and 14 green
    party hats. How many hats did she make in all? _____

11. Carlos brought 28 noisemakers for the party.
    Half were purple and half were pink.
    How many of each color were there? _____

Reproducible HP101

Month Mix-Up

Happy New Year! Father Time dropped his calendar pages and needs your help. Number them from 1 to 12 in the correct order.

Soup Search

January is Soup Month! Look into this steaming bowl of alphabet soup and follow the directions.

Color the letters that spell **warm** yellow.
Color the letters that spell **good** red.
Color the letters that spell **filling** blue.
Color the letters that spell **nutritious** green.

HP101

Dragon Dance

There are many ways to welcome in the Chinese New Year! One is to dance beneath a long paper dragon. Solve the math equations. Use the same colors to match the parts of the dragon with the lanterns.

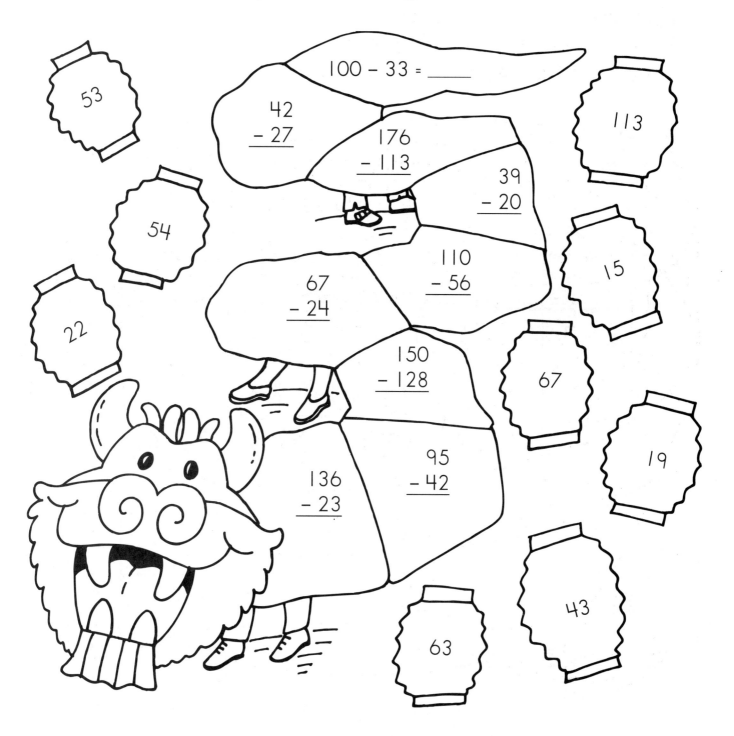

$$100 - 33 = \underline{\hspace{1cm}}$$

$$\begin{array}{r} 42 \\ -\ 27 \\ \hline \end{array}$$

$$\begin{array}{r} 176 \\ -\ 113 \\ \hline \end{array}$$

$$\begin{array}{r} 39 \\ -\ 20 \\ \hline \end{array}$$

$$\begin{array}{r} 67 \\ -\ 24 \\ \hline \end{array}$$

$$\begin{array}{r} 110 \\ -\ 56 \\ \hline \end{array}$$

$$\begin{array}{r} 150 \\ -\ 128 \\ \hline \end{array}$$

$$\begin{array}{r} 136 \\ -\ 23 \\ \hline \end{array}$$

$$\begin{array}{r} 95 \\ -\ 42 \\ \hline \end{array}$$

Lanterns: 53, 113, 54, 15, 22, 67, 19, 63, 43

HP101

Name _____   Date _____

Special Speech

In January we remember a man named Martin Luther King, Jr. He wanted everyone to be treated equally. Use the grid below to discover something he said during his famous speech.

" _____   _____ "

♡-3   ♥-2 ■-5 △-7 ●-5   ○-1   □-9 ▲-6 ♥-9 △-4 ●-8

	1	2	3	4	5	6	7	8	9	10
▲	B	T	T	E	W	R	I	U	B	Y
♡	S	N	I	D	R	Y	X	A	L	V
■	E	S	X	H	A	I	M	T	Q	L
○	A	G	I	E	U	H	C	N	M	D
△	W	K	P	A	L	Q	V	B	M	P
♥	F	H	P	N	A	C	Z	J	E	Z
□	G	F	Q	U	O	Q	S	W	D	J
●	J	Y	G	R	E	X	K	M	Y	K

HP101

Name _____   Date _____

✓ Snowflake Math

Cut out the snowflakes. Use them to make number sentences.

_____ + _____ = _____

_____ + _____ = _____

_____ + _____ = _____

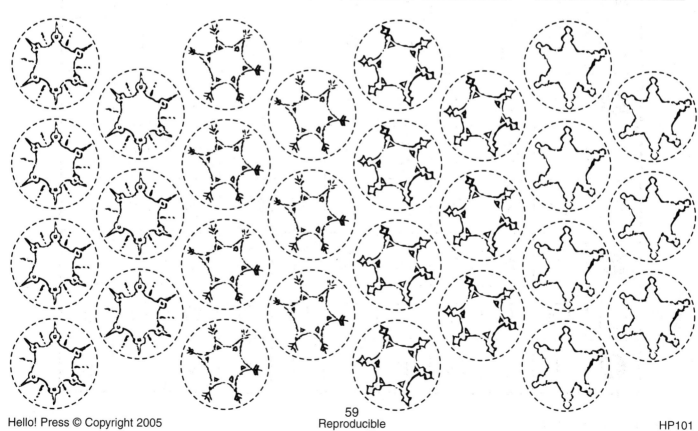

Name _____ Date _____

I Have a Dream

Martin Luther King, Jr. was a great civil rights leader. He gave a famous speech about his dream of freedom and justice for everyone. Celebrate his birthday by finding the words in the puzzle.

Martin
Luther
King
America
dream
equal
freedom
hope
justice
liberty
peace
rights
truth

```
L  I  B  E  R  T  Y  D  M  Y
U  I  N  K  I  N  G  E  A  B
T  F  J  C  G  R  D  Q  R  A
H  R  U  C  H  T  R  U  T  H
E  E  S  R  T  E  N  A  I  O
R  E  T  A  S  E  E  L  N  P
O  D  I  L  A  P  E  A  C  E
A  O  C  J  D  R  E  A  M  M
A  M  E  R  I  C  A  U  S  A
```

I have a dream that someday everyone will live together in peace.

HP101

Name _____   Date _____

Snow Globes

Materials needed:

small glass jars with lids (like baby food jars or slightly larger)
small plastic figures that fit inside the jars (people, animals, dinosaurs,
    trees, etc.)
small shiny rocks
glitter
water
epoxy glue
hot glue gun

Directions:

1. Let children select the figures, rocks, etc., they would like in their
    snow globes.
2. Use the hot glue gun to glue rocks and plastic figures to the bottom
    of the jar. **This step must be done by an adult.**
3. Fill the jar almost completely with water.
4. Add a spoonful of glitter.
5. Use epoxy glue to secure the lid. **This step must be done by an adult.**
6. Shake the jar to make it snow!

If you have enough time and material, let children make several snow
globes as gifts for friends and relatives.

HP101

Name _____ Date _____

Where Do You Live?

1. Trace the outline of the United States in blue.

2. Color your state red.

3. Make a black dot to show the city where you live.

4. Write the names of two states that border on your state.

   _____   _____

5. Write the names of two states that are near an ocean.

   _____   _____

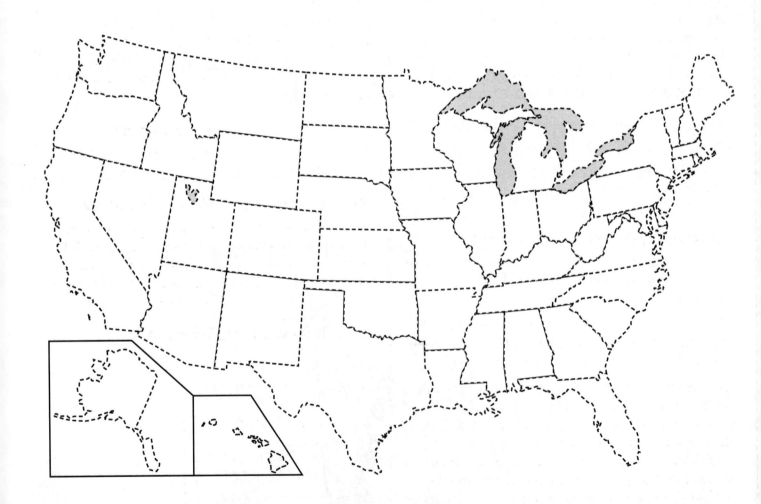

HP101

Historical Happenings (Activity)

February is Black History Month, a time to commemorate African-Americans who have changed the world.

Celebrating Black History began in 1926, when Dr. Carter G. Woodson, a Harvard Ph.D., initiated "Negro History Week." Dr. Woodson, a historian, chose the second week in February because it included the birthdays of Frederick Douglass and Abraham Lincoln. In 1976, the weeklong observance was extended to the entire month of February to provide more time for celebratory programs and activities.

Use a search engine such as _www.yahoo.com_ or _www.looksmart.com_ and type in the key words _Black History Month_ to find a multitude of websites featuring related suggestions, activities, and lesson plans. This site has some excellent, age-appropriate material: _http://www.enchantedlearning.com/history/us/aframer/_

February Facts (Activity Extension)

Make a copy of this page for each child and one for the group. Each day, ask one child to share what he or she wrote that day and write that on the group copy.

Groundhog Day Game (Activity)

Give each child two 3" x 5" index cards. Ask them to decorate one with a sunny scene and one with a cloudy scene.

All children need to stand to begin the game. Select one child to be the "groundhog" and have that child put his or her two cards in a brown paper bag.

Ask the others to guess what the "groundhog" will predict by holding up one of their pictures. The child who is the groundhog selects one card from the bag without looking and shows it to the class. All children who match the card selected remain standing and play the next round. Those who do not match the prediction sit down.

Return the card to the bag and shake. Continue until only one child matches the groundhog's prediction. That child becomes the "groundhog" for the next game.

Valentine Gifts (Directions)

Make several copies of this page for each child. Use red, pink, or other pastel-colored construction paper. On each valentine, have children write or draw something they will give or do for family members. Examples: the words _3 hugs_ or picture of child taking out the trash, sweeping, shoveling, etc.

Add Up the Presidents (Activity Extension)

Cut out coupons for fast-food restaurants or grocery stores that have prices, like 2 biscuits for $1.99 or apples, 3 pounds for $1.98. Have them select two items they might like to buy and add up the total cost.

Add Up the Presidents (Answers)

A. 7¢; B. 11¢; C. 15¢; D. 13¢; E. 17¢; F. 10¢; G. 30¢; H. 23¢; I. 41¢

More Practice with Money (Activity)

Use play coins to help children count money, add, and subtract coins, and make change. Let one child pretend to purchase items with the coupons and pay for them with play money. Another child can be the clerk and make the correct change.

Which Pet Is Best? (Solution)

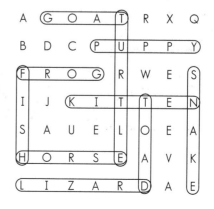

Historical Happenings

Dr. Carter G. Woodson began Black History Month to honor African-Americans and their contributions to American history.

Start at the dates and trace each line with a different colored crayon to learn four important February events.

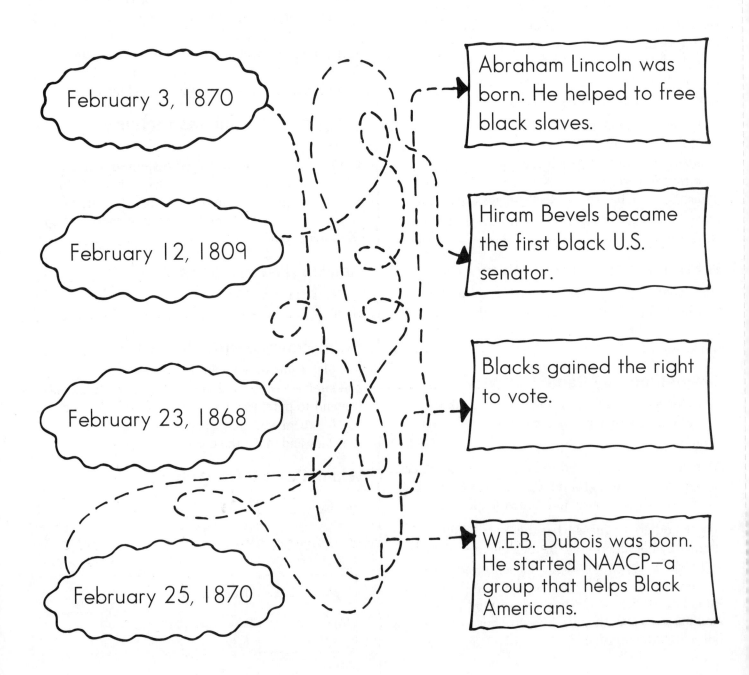

February 3, 1870

February 12, 1809

February 23, 1868

February 25, 1870

Abraham Lincoln was born. He helped to free black slaves.

Hiram Bevels became the first black U.S. senator.

Blacks gained the right to vote.

W.E.B. Dubois was born. He started NAACP—a group that helps Black Americans.

HP101

Name _____ Date _____

February Facts

Everyone should learn something new every day. Each day this month, write something new you learned. It could be a new word, an interesting fact, or even a good joke.

February 1	February 15
February 2	February 16
February 3	February 17
February 4	February 18
February 5	February 19
February 6	February 20
February 7	February 21
February 8	February 22
February 9	February 23
February 10	February 24
February 11	February 25
February 12	February 26
February 13	February 27
February 14	February 28

Reproducible
HP101

Time to Visit friends

Draw a line from each sentence to the clock with the same time.

Rabbit took a basket of eggs to Mrs. Hen at 9:00.

Mrs. Hen went to visit Mr. Green at 10:00.

Mr. Green took flowers to Mrs. Fern at 9:30.

Mrs. Fern gave Ms. Daisy a loaf of homemade
bread at 8:00.

Ms. Daisy took Rose and Lily to the park
at 10:30.

Rose and Lily made an Easter card for Rabbit
at 8:30.

Mr. Duck went to Rabbit's house at 8:15.

Write the answers.

What time did Rose and Lily go to the park?_____

What happened at 8:00? _____

_____

What did Rose and Lily make for Rabbit?_____

What did Mr. Green take to Mrs. Fern? _____

HP101

Name _____ Date _____

The Groundhog Predicts

Some people believe that if the groundhog sees its shadow on February 2, we will have six more weeks of bad winter weather. If it doesn't see its shadow, spring will come soon.

What if a groundhog could predict other things besides weather?

Write a question for the groundhog. Then draw the answer in the crystal ball.

My question for the groundhog is: _____

_____

HP101

One Word from Two

Compound words are two words joined together to make new words. Join the words from Box 1 with words from Box 2 to make new words. Use all words from Box 2 at least once.

Box 1	ball	snow	sun	time

Box 2

any	spring	screen	over	lamp	fall	tan	plow	flake
day	ball	storm	set	pin	life	bed	soft	man
flower	dial	basket	suit	shoes	play	fish	winter	rise
meal	foot	drift	base	summer	shine	light	burn	some
roof	night	hard	eye	beam				

snow words _snowball_ _____

_____

sun words _sunflower_ _____

_____

ball words _football_ _____

_____

time words _daytime_ _____

_____

HP101

Name _____   Date _____

February 2 Is Groundhog Day

Find these words in the puzzle. The words go across or down.

SEE

THE

GROUNDHOG

LOOK

FOR

HIS

SHADOW

How many words can you make using the letters in the word **groundhog**?
Write your words on the lines.

_____   _____

_____   _____

_____   _____

_____   _____

Count the number of words you made. Write the total. _____

HP101

Valentine Math

1. Kym cut out 17 red hearts and 6 pink hearts. How many hearts in all?

   _____

2. Ned gave his mother 12 blue flowers and 9 white flowers. How many flowers did he give his mother?

   _____

3. Cassie arranged her valentines in three rows. She put four in each row. Draw a picture to show Cassie's valentines.

4. Matt, Toby, and Lisa blew up balloons for a party. Each one blew up 6 balloons. Draw a picture to show how many balloons in all.

5. The Valentine party started at one o'clock. It lasted two hours. Show what time it was over.

Knock, knock.
Who's there?
Wheel.
Wheel who?
"Wheel" you be my valentine?

HP101

Valentine Gifts

Parents and Teachers: See page 63 for directions on how to complete this page.

Reproducible

HP101

Presidents' Day

Match the Presidents' names with their pictures.

Thomas Jefferson   John F. Kennedy   Abraham Lincoln

Franklin Roosevelt   George Washington

Make change.

You have:	**You spend:**	**How much left?** Write the amount.
	15¢	_____
	12¢	_____
	29¢	_____
  	13¢	_____

HP101

Name _____ Date _____

Add Up the Presidents

Add the coins. Write the total amounts.

A.   = _____

B.   = _____

C.   = _____

D.    = _____

E.   = _____

F.   = _____

G.   = _____

H.   = _____

I.   = _____

HP101

Which Pet Is Best?

Circle the names of the pets.

A	G	O	A	T	R	X	Q
B	D	C	P	U	P	P	Y
F	R	O	G	R	W	E	S
I	J	K	I	T	T	E	N
S	A	U	E	L	O	E	A
H	O	R	S	E	A	V	K
L	I	Z	A	R	D	A	E

FISH
FROG
GOAT
KITTEN
LIZARD
HORSE
PUPPY
SNAKE
TOAD
TURTLE

1. Which pet do you think is best? _____

2. Draw a picture of you and a pet you have or would like to have.

Celebrate Dr. Seuss's Birthday (Activity)

Celebrate on March 3 by reading Dr. Seuss stories to the children. Encourage them to draw pictures from favorite Dr. Seuss books or write their own stories in Dr. Seuss style.

National Anthem Day (Activity)

Celebrate National Anthem Day on March 3 by teaching children the words to "The Star-Spangled Banner" and singing it together.

Crazy Clocks (Solution)

It's April Fools' Day!

Celebrate St. Patrick's Day (Activity)

Celebrate St. Patrick's Day with snacks that are green, like celery, green grapes, green apple slices, etc. Add green food coloring to change the color of some foods or drinks that usually aren't green.

Do They Hatch from Eggs? (Pre-Activity)

Before completing the activity, ask children these questions and talk about the answers as a group.

Are birds the only animals that hatch from eggs?
(No, many other types of animals hatch from eggs.)

Do all birds hatch from eggs, even penguins and ostriches? (Yes)

Do mammals (animals with fur) hatch from eggs?
(No—except one, the platypus.)

Do all fish hatch from eggs?
(No. Some types do. Some don't.)

Do whales hatch from eggs?
(No, whales are mammals.)

What other animals hatch from eggs?
(Let children list as many as possible: alligators, snakes, turtles, insects, toads, frogs, etc.)

What's Green? (Follow-Up Activity)

After children complete the activity, talk about what they drew that isn't usually green and how strange it looks to see that object the "wrong" color. Talk about foods that aren't supposed to be eaten when they are green—like peaches, bread, milk, orange juice, etc. Ask children if they think those items would taste differently if they were green. Try an experiment. Add a few drops of green food coloring to white milk. Stir and drink. Does the milk taste different? (Although most people think it tastes different, food coloring will not change the taste of milk unless it is flavored.)

Spring Word Search (Solution)

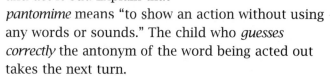

Antonym Charades (Activity Extension)

Write words from the antonym activity page on slips of paper. Have one child select a word and act it out. Explain that *pantomime* means "to show an action without using any words or sounds." The child who *guesses correctly* the antonym of the word being acted out takes the next turn.

Get a Jump-Start on Spring (Activity)

Let children plant flower or vegetable seeds in small pots or Styrofoam™ cups filled about three-quarters full of potting soil. Have them observe and chart the growth of the seeds. To do this easily, number each pot and write the name of the type of seed in each pot on the chart. Remind them that plants need water and sunshine to grow. Tie this in with a unit on plants.

When the sprouts are ready and the weather is warm enough, help children transplant the seedlings outside.

It's a Spring Thing! (Answers)

9 flowers, 4 butterflies, 2 ducks, 4 birds, 1 rabbit, 6 frogs

Crazy Clocks

Hi! My name is Andy and this is my dog, Cuddles. We set all the clocks in our house at different times. Use the code to find why we did this.

S = 5

R = 10   I = 20   O = 30   T = 40   D = 50

F = 15   P = 25   A = 35   L = 45   Y = 55

___	___	___	,	___	___	___	___	___
20	40	5		35	25	10	20	45

___	___	___	___	___	,	___	___	___
15	30	30	45	5		50	35	55	!

HP101

Language Arts: Creative Writing

Happy St. Patrick's Day

Color the leprechaun. Inside the shamrock, write a short poem or story about meeting a leprechaun.

HP101

Name _____   Date _____

Shamrock Math

Add.

	2		7		5		9
	+8		+5		+6		+3

	22		77		34		46
	+36		+11		+43		+53

	231		121		631		810
	+35		+73		+26		+47

Subtract.

	7		6		12		5
	-5		-3		-5		-4

	99		100		55		120
	-77		-50		-44		-50

Reproducible

HP101

Name _____   Date _____

Do They Hatch from Eggs?

Color the animals that hatch from eggs.

HP101

What's Green?

Green is the color of spring and St. Patrick's Day. List 12 things that
are green.

1. _____
2. _____
3. _____
4. _____
5. _____   9. _____
6. _____   10. _____
7. _____   11. _____
8. _____   12. _____

Draw something green you like to eat.

Draw something that isn't usually green, but color it green anyway.

Arts and Crafts/Creative Thinking

What's in the Egg?

This egg is about to hatch. Draw a picture to show what you think is inside.

HP101

Pinwheels

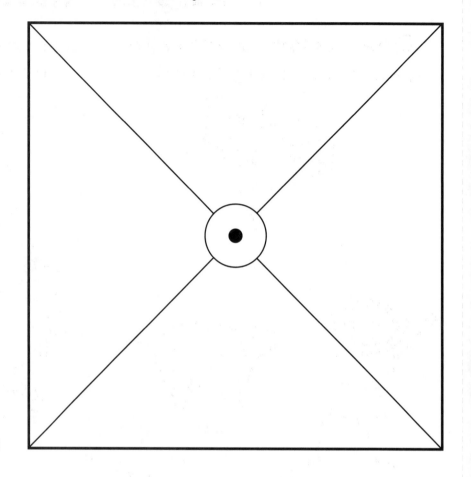

Supplies

pinwheel pattern
thumbtack
drinking straw or narrow
    wooden dowel
scissors
tape
markers or crayons

Procedure

1. Cut out the square.

2. Decorate your
   pinwheel with markers
   or crayons.

3. Cut down each line. Stop at
   the center in the circle.

4. Bend the right point of
   each flap to the black dot
   in the center. Secure flaps
   with a tiny piece of tape.

5. Attach pinwheel to the dowel or
   straw with a thumbtack. Don't push
   the thumbtack all the way in, or the
   pinwheel will not be able to spin freely.

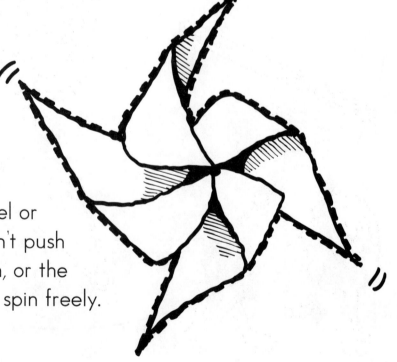

HP101

Kite or Wind?

Draw lines from the kite to the pictures with a long **i** sound.

Draw lines from the wind to pictures with a short **i** sound.

pig

child

chick

fish

knife

mitt

bike

dime

lion

pin

ice cube

HP101

Name _____ Date _____

Spring Word Search

Look up and down to find the words hidden in the puzzle.

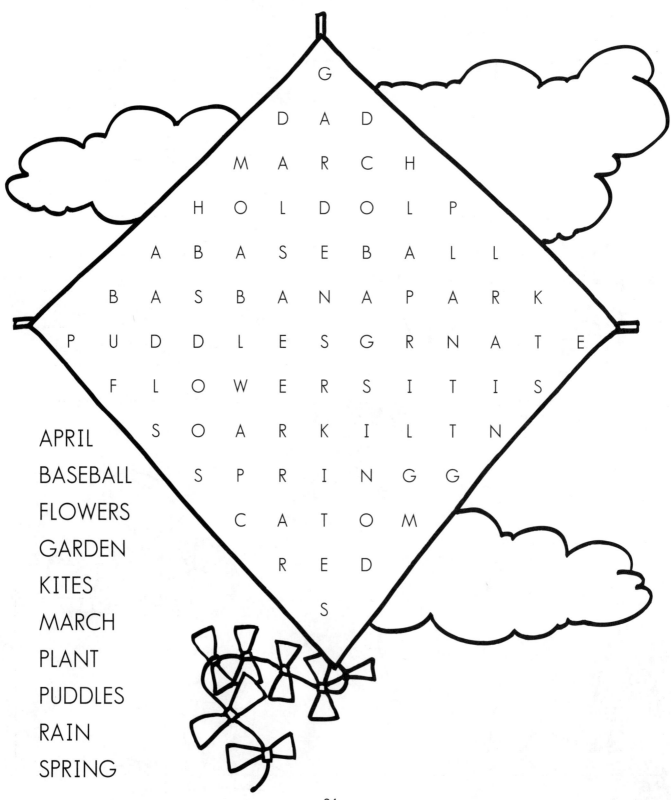

APRIL

BASEBALL

FLOWERS

GARDEN

KITES

MARCH

PLANT

PUDDLES

RAIN

SPRING

HP101

Name _____ Date _____

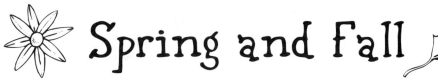

Spring and Fall

Antonyms are words that mean the opposite, like **spring** and **fall**.

Write an antonym for each word.

bad	_____	big	_____
boy	_____	small	_____
few	_____	stop	_____
cold	_____	give	_____
sleep	_____	inside	_____
work	_____	under	_____
push	_____	front	_____
wrong	_____	child	_____
sad	_____	laugh	_____
far	_____	day	_____
light	_____	slow	_____
bottom	_____	her	_____

Draw two pictures that are opposite of each other.

Reproducible
HP101

Name _____   Date _____

It's a Spring Thing!

Springtime means blue skies, warm weather, and sunshine! Count the flowers, birds, butterflies, bunnies, ducks, and frogs. Write those numbers next to the pictures below. Color the picture.

HP101

Getting Ready for Easter (Answers)

bunnies, hurry, getting, hopping, putting, eggs, cooperating

What's in the Egg? (Activity Extension)

Give each child a plastic egg and ask him or her to put a small object in it when no one is looking. Let children take turns in front of the class. Have them shake the egg and see if anyone can guess what's inside. If not, have the child give a clue and let the others guess again.

Baseball Math (Answers)

1. 21; 2. 3; 3. 8; 4. 120; 5. 16; 6.10:30 A.M.; 7.14; 8. 5

Compound Capers (Answers)

1. sailboat; 2. Sunday; 3. toybox; 4. flashlight; 5. rainbow; 6. sidewalk; 7. daydream; 8. watermelon; 9. strawberry; 10. footprint; 11. bluebird; 12. butterfly

More Compound Capers (Activity)

Copy, laminate, and cut out the word cards. Make additional cards with words that can be joined to make compound words.

Let children mix and match the cards to make compound words. Point out that some words like *day* could be used at the beginning of a compound word (daytime) or at the end (Sunday).

More or Less? (Answers)

1. >; 2. =; 3. <; 4. <; 5. =; 6. =; 7. >; 8. <; 9. =; 10. <; 11. =; 12. =

Baseball Time (Activity Extension)

Ask children to write baseball story problems using addition or subtraction of time or money. (If one hot dog costs $1.50, how much will two hot dogs cost?) Let them trade papers and solve each other's story problems.

How Does Your Garden Grow? (Activity)

Let children start their own indoor flower gardens by planting marigold or other flower seeds in small plastic pots or Styrofoam™ cups. Remind them to water their plants twice a week and provide plenty of sun. Help children make charts to record the growth of their plants.

Earth Day Equation (Answer)

Total is 49.

Simon Says, "Hop like a bunny." (Activity)

Play Simon Says in the gym or on the playground. Give directions for bunny motions.

Suggestions: Simon says:

Take six bunny hops to your left (right, backwards, forwards).

Wiggle your nose like a bunny four times.

Thump your left (or right) foot three times.

Wiggle your ears like a bunny.

April Is National Humor Month (Activity)

Since April 1 is April Fools' Day, it's a great time to start celebrating National Humor Month. Provide several books of jokes and riddles in your Reading Center. Ask two or three children to share their favorite jokes and riddles with the group each day.

Play a harmless April Fools' joke on children by making some silly changes to the classroom before they arrive on April 1. Do some silly, unexpected things during the day, such as wearing a silly hat, writing a sentence backwards on the chalkboard, or wearing your clothes inside out. Tell them you are going to give them a spelling test, then, very seriously, ask them to spell words that are way too difficult, such as ambivalence, gargantuan, inestimable, chrysanthemum, or supercalifragilistic-expialidocious.

Getting Ready for Easter

Choose the double set of letters on the paint jars to finish the words. They help tell what's going on in this factory! Color the picture.

What a bunch of busy bu ___ ___ ies! They are in a hu ___ ___ y!

They are ge ___ ___ ing baskets ready for Easter Morning.

Some are ho ___ ___ ing back and forth. Others are pu ___ ___ ing

colored e ___ ___ s in a line. They are c ___ ___ perating to

get the job done!

HP101

Baseball Math

1. The Red team made 12 home runs. The Blue team made 9 home runs. How many home runs in all? _____

2. How many more home runs did the Red team make? _____

3. There were 17 children on the Red team. Nine team members were on the field. How many team members sat on the bench? _____

4. Jacob and Sara were the Red team's best hitters. Jacob had 72 hits during the season. Sara had 48 hits. How many hits did Jacob and Sara have in all? _____

5. The Blue team played two games a week for eight weeks. How many games did they play in all? _____

6. The Blue team practiced for an hour and a half every Tuesday morning. They started practice at 9 A.M. What time did they finish? _____

7. Tasha had 63 hits during the season. Her twin sister, Rachel, had 49 hits. How many more hits did Tasha have? _____

8. The coach for the Green team brought two dozen cartons of juice to the game. Players drank 19 cartons. How many cartons were left? _____

Write a baseball math story. Trade papers with a partner and solve.

9. _____

_____

_____

_____

HP101

Name _____ Date _____

Compound Capers

Compound words are two words joined together to make new words.

Add a word from the box to each word below to make compound words.

berry	bird	boat	bow
box	day	dream	fly
light	melon	print	walk

Example: fish + ____hook____ = ____fishhook____

1. sail + _____ = _____
2. Sun + _____ = _____
3. toy + _____ = _____
4. flash + _____ = _____
5. rain + _____ = _____
6. side + _____ = _____
7. day + _____ = _____
8. water + _____ = _____
9. straw + _____ = _____
10. foot + _____ = _____
11. blue + _____ = _____
12. butter + _____ = _____

Write more compound words:

_____   _____   _____

_____   _____   _____

HP101

More Compound Capers

stop	light	sign
some	day	thing
note	book	bag
time	light	cup
cake	lady	bug
any	body	no
base	foot	ball
snow	basket	step

(Parents and Teachers: See page 87 for directions.)

HP101

More or Less?

Write the correct symbol > (greater than) < (less than) or = (equal) between each pair of eggs.

1. 564 _____ 456

2. 7 + 12 _____ 19

3. 20 - 10 _____ 11

4. 17 - 4 _____ 12 + 4

5. 68 _____ 54 + 14

6. 8 + 8 _____ 9 + 7

7. 1,126 _____ 1,112

8. 7,435 _____ 7,453

9. 16 + 16 _____ 32

10. 19 - 11 _____ 10

11. 98 - 8 _____ 80 + 10

12. 100 - 50 _____ 25 + 25

HP101

Baseball Time

Draw hands on the clock to show each time.

The team got on the bus at 10:30 A.M.

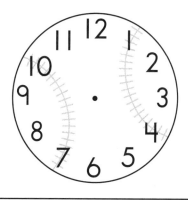

The team ate lunch at 12:30.

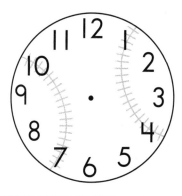

The game began at 2:00 P.M.

A new pitcher took over at 3:15 P.M.

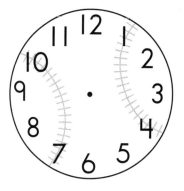

Jeremy had a hot dog with chili at 3:30 P.M.

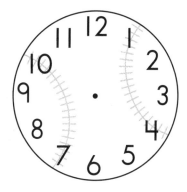

The game ended an hour later. Show what time the game ended.

HP101

Name _____   Date _____

Where Do They Live?

Color the animals blue if they can only live in water.

Color the animals red if they live only on land.

Color the animals green if they live on land and in water.

HP101

April Showers Bring May Flowers

Color the raindrops that have words with the long vowel **a** sound.

Name _____   Date _____

Earth Day Equation

Earth Day is a time for us to remember what an awesome planet we live on! It's important for us to keep it clean and beautiful! Air pollution, acid rain, and holes in the ozone layer hurt the earth. Sharpen your pencil, get some scratch paper, and figure out the tricky math equation shown.

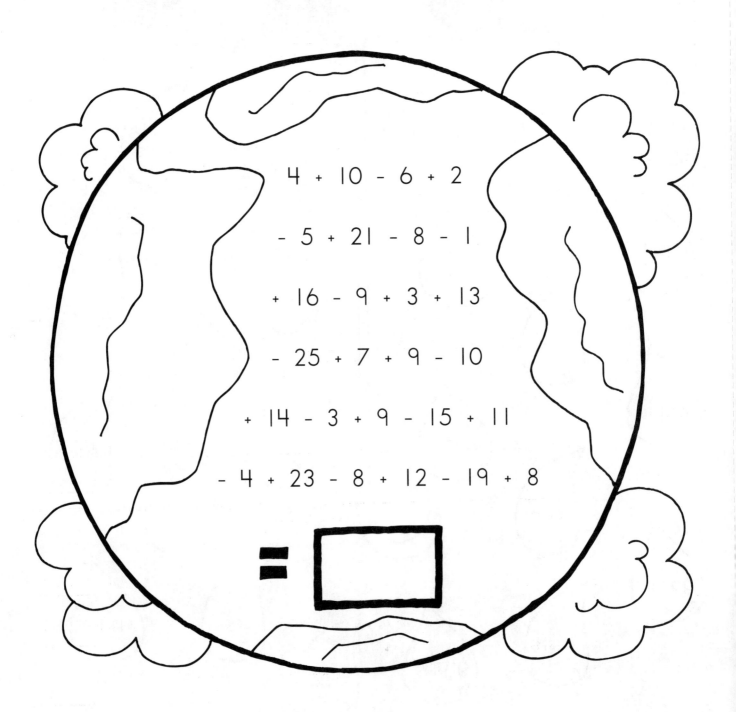

$$4 + 10 - 6 + 2$$
$$- 5 + 21 - 8 - 1$$
$$+ 16 - 9 + 3 + 13$$
$$- 25 + 7 + 9 - 10$$
$$+ 14 - 3 + 9 - 15 + 11$$
$$- 4 + 23 - 8 + 12 - 19 + 8$$
$$= \boxed{}$$

HP101

Flowers from the Heart (Directions)

Let children cut heart shapes from pieces of colored paper; they can use scraps of wallpaper, wrapping paper, etc., for lots of variety.

Children can draw flower stems with green crayons or markers on large sheets of white construction paper.

Have children assemble their flowers by gluing the hearts in place for the leaves and flower petals around the poems.

Ask children to write a flower poem on scrap paper. They can write the final draft on the lined circles. This would make a great gift for May Day.

Mother Goose Day (Activity Extension)

May 1 is Mother Goose Day, a day to remember and share the nursery rhymes we loved as children.

Before children complete this activity, say each of the nursery rhymes with them. After they draw their pictures, children can take turns showing their drawings to the class. Let classmates guess the nursery rhyme portrayed.

Cinco de Mayo (Activity)

Celebrate Cinco de Mayo on May 5 with a party. Include mariachi music, a parade, decorations, and Mexican food.

Museum Day (Activity)

Celebrate Museum Day on May 18 by taking children on a field trip to a local museum. Invite children to create their own classroom museum of seeds, rocks, leaves, and other items they can collect, label, and display.

Mother's Day Coupons (Pre-Activity)

Before children complete this activity, ask them to suggest ideas of special things they can do for their moms. Talk about why moms are special and the many ways they help their children. For any children without a mom, encourage them to talk about another special woman in their lives, like an older sister, grandmother, stepmother, or aunt.

Make a Family Tree (Activity Extension)

Let children work with parents to fill in the names on the family tree. They can draw in extra branches if needed for a stepparent. Complete the rest of the activity in class.

After cutting and gluing the tree to colored construction paper, invite children to make a decorative border and add flowers, drawings of family members, or other details.

Happy Mother's Day (Extension Activity)

Encourage children to make their own cards and gifts for Mother's Day. An offer to help with chores around the house or yard is always a great gift.

Marvelous Memories (Answer)

Memorial Day

Memorial Day at the Lake (Answers)

1. 13; 2. 23 feet; 3. 27; 4. 17; 5. 33; 6. 11; 7. 16; 8. 7:40 A.M.; 9.22 inches

Bike Safely (Extension Activity)

Let children take turns reading their bike safety rules. Use this opportunity to talk about other outdoor recreation safety rules for skating, swimming, playing baseball, etc. Rather than simply stating rules, talk about the reasons behind the rules so children understand how the rules help keep people safe.

Flowers from the Heart

HP101

Name _____ Date _____

Mother Goose Day

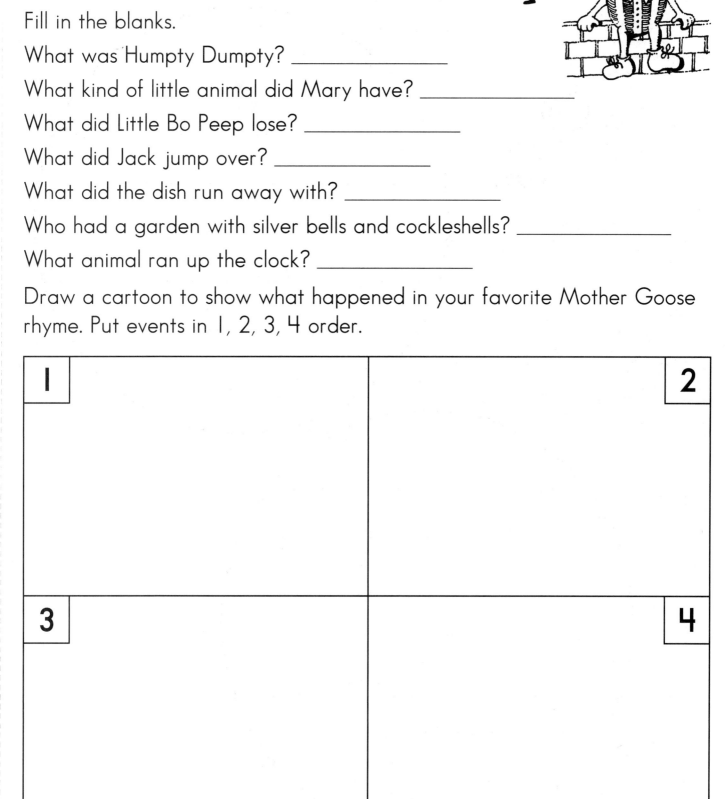

Fill in the blanks.

What was Humpty Dumpty? _____

What kind of little animal did Mary have? _____

What did Little Bo Peep lose? _____

What did Jack jump over? _____

What did the dish run away with? _____

Who had a garden with silver bells and cockleshells? _____

What animal ran up the clock? _____

Draw a cartoon to show what happened in your favorite Mother Goose rhyme. Put events in 1, 2, 3, 4 order.

1	2
3	4

In the Merry Month of May

Use the May calendar to answer the questions.

Sunday	Monday	Tuesday	Wednesday	Thursday	Friday	Saturday
	1 May Day Mother Goose Day	2	3	4 New Moon ●	5 Cinco de Mayo	6
7	8 Furry Dance Day in Helston, England	9	10 ◗ First Quarter	11	12 Limerick Day	13
14 Mother's Day	15	16	17	18 ○ Full Moon Museum Day	19	20 Armed Forces Day
21 Lindbergh Flight Day	22	23	24	25	26 ◖ Last Quarter	27
28	29 Memorial Day	30	31			

What day of the week is Mother's Day on? _____

What is the date of Armed Forces Day? _____

What two events are celebrated on May 1? _____

_____

How many days after Museum Day until Memorial Day? _____

Cinco de Mayo is a holiday in Mexico. When is it celebrated? _____

Charles Lindbergh was the first person to fly an airplane across
the Atlantic Ocean alone. What day is named for him? _____

On May 24, 1883, the Brooklyn Bridge in New York opened. Write
Brooklyn Bridge Day on the calendar.

Name _____ Date _____

How Does Your Garden Grow?

Many people plant gardens in May. Draw six things you would like to plant in a garden.

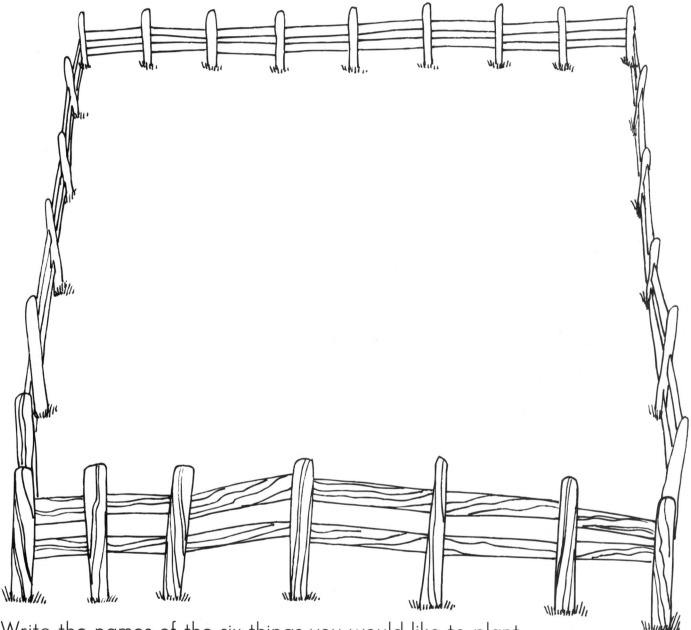

Write the names of the six things you would like to plant.

_____   _____

_____   _____

_____   _____

HP101

Mother's Day Coupons

Mother's Day is for moms and other special women in your life.

To give that special person a great Mother's Day gift, fill in the coupons. On each one, write a promise of something special you will do for her, like sharing three big hugs, watching your little brother or sister for an hour, or helping with jobs around the house.

Decorate the coupons with crayons, markers, or colored pencils.

Dear _____,

My special gift to you on Mother's Day is

_____

Love,

_____

Dear _____,

This Mother's Day coupon is good for

_____

Love,

_____

Dear _____,

My special gift to you on Mother's Day is

_____

Love,

_____

Name _____ Date _____

Make a Family Tree

Fill in the names. Color the tree. Cut out the tree and glue it to colored construction paper.

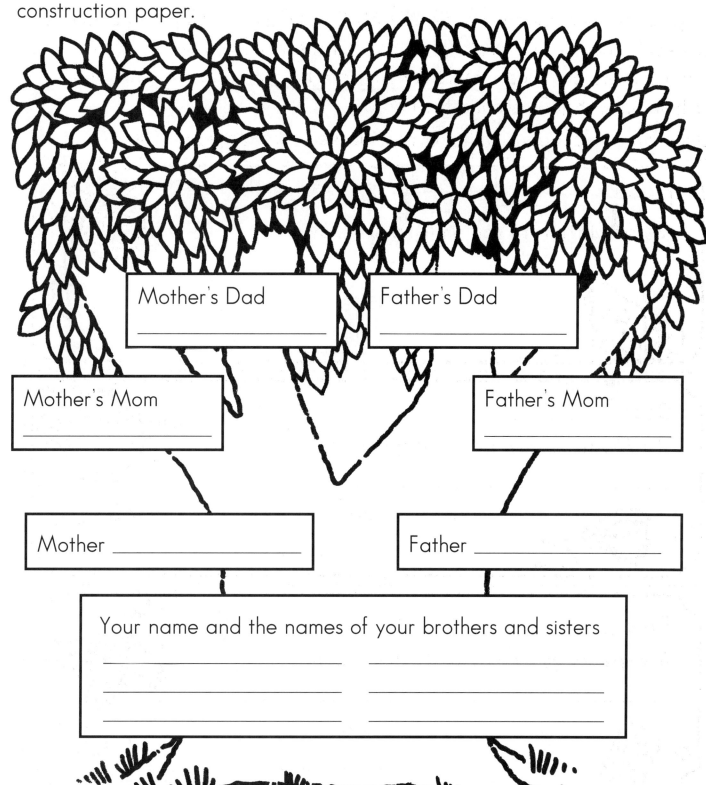

Mother's Dad
_____

Father's Dad
_____

Mother's Mom
_____

Father's Mom
_____

Mother _____

Father _____

Your name and the names of your brothers and sisters

_____   _____

_____   _____

_____   _____

Name _____ Date _____

Which Way Should They Go?

Jill and Josh are meeting friends for a picnic at Memorial Park. They need directions on how to get from their house to the park. Study the map. Then write directions for them. Use direction words like **left**, **right**, **north**, **south**, **east**, and **west**.

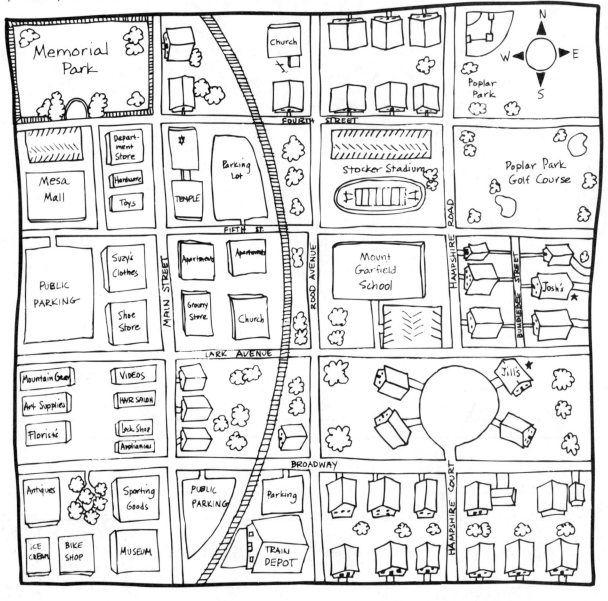

_____

_____

_____

HP101

Name _____ Date _____

Marvelous Memories

An important occasion happens at the end of May. Read what it's about below. Then finish filling in the boxes, from top to bottom, with this same phrase. When you're finished, the name of this holiday will be spelled across the page.

TIME TO REMEMBER LOVED
FRIENDS AND FAMILY

HP101

Memorial Day at the Lake

Write the equations and answers.

1. Nine red boats and four blue boats sailed on the lake. _____
    How many boats were on the lake?

2. The boat named Lazy Daze was 37 feet long. Another _____
    boat, Summer Sun, was 14 feet long. How much longer
    was Lazy Daze?

3. Fourteen boys and 13 girls jumped in the lake to swim. _____
    How many were in the lake?

4. After an hour, 4 boys and 6 girls went back to shore. _____
    How many children were still in the lake?

5. The Johnson triplets hunted for shells. Jerry found 9, Jeff _____
    found 11, and Joann found 13. How many shells did
    they find in all?

6. If they shared all the shells equally, how many shells _____
    would each one have?

7. Pam caught 7 fish in the morning and 9 fish after lunch. _____
    How many fish did she catch in all?

8. Pam started fishing at 5:30 A.M. She fished for two _____
    hours and ten minutes. What time did she stop fishing?

9. Cal built a sand castle 14 inches high. Kira's castle was _____
    8 inches higher. How high was Kira's sand castle?

10. Write your own math story question about the lake.

    _____

    _____

    _____

HP101

Name _____   Date _____

Bike Safely

Bike riding is great fun when the weather is nice. Write four bike safety rules everyone should follow. Color the picture.

Bike Safety Rules

1. _____

_____

2. _____

_____

3. _____

_____

4. _____

_____

HP101

June Is Dairy Month (Solution)

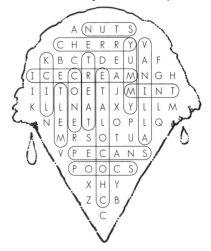

June Is Dairy Month (Activity Extension)

Use this opportunity to talk about the food pyramid and the importance of eating healthy.

Flag Day (Activity)

Celebrate Flag Day on June 14. Let children color the flags. Display the flags in your window or let children tape them to dowels and march in a parade.

The decorated flags could also be used for a Memorial Day celebration.

Pledge of Allegiance (Activity)

Celebrate Flag Day by teaching children the words to the Pledge of Allegiance. Discuss the meaning of words like *justice, allegiance, indivisible,* and *pledge.*

> I pledge allegiance to the flag of the United States of America, and to the Republic for which it stands, one Nation, under God, indivisible, with liberty and justice for all.

Happy Father's Day (Activity Extension)

Encourage children to make their own cards and gifts for Father's Day. An offer to help with chores around the house or yard is also a great gift.

Eating Healthy (Examples)

Fats and sweets include cookies, cakes, pies, doughnuts, and "junk food" with empty calories, like potato chips.

Proteins include types of meat, poultry, fish, dry beans, eggs, and nuts.

Dairy products include milk, cheese, yogurt, and other products made from milk.

Starches include bread, cereals, rice, pasta, and other grain products.

Ask children to name foods that contain items from two or more food groups, like a sausage pizza: tomato sauce (vegetable), cheese (dairy), crust (starches), and sausage (meat).

Summer Safety (Answer)

Always wear your helmet when biking or skating.

Who Took the Vowels? (Answers)

1. golf
2. soccer
3. hockey
4. tennis
5. basketball
6. football
7. skiing
8. skating
9. bowling
10. swimming

Summer Words (Activity Extension)

Ask children to brainstorm for more "summer words." Write their words on chart paper and read the list together when you finish.

Time for Fun (Pre-Activity)

Before completing this activity, begin by counting together by fives. Review telling time with an analog clock. Many children rely on digital clocks and fail to develop this basic skill.

HP101

Name _____   Date _____

June Is Dairy Month

Look up and down to find the ice cream words in the cone.

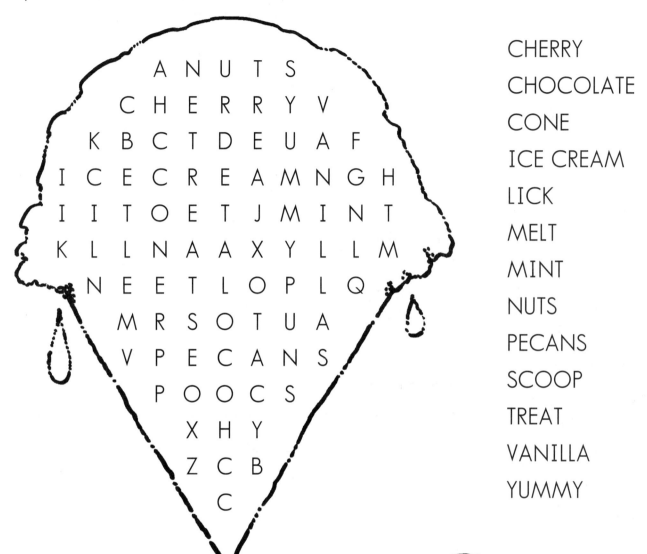

CHERRY
CHOCOLATE
CONE
ICE CREAM
LICK
MELT
MINT
NUTS
PECANS
SCOOP
TREAT
VANILLA
YUMMY

Foods made from milk are called dairy foods. Color the pictures of dairy foods.

Flag Day

The U.S. flag has 50 white stars on a blue background. Each star represents a state. Color the background around the stars dark blue.

The 13 red and white stripes represent the first 13 colonies of the United States. Color the first stripe and every other stripe red.

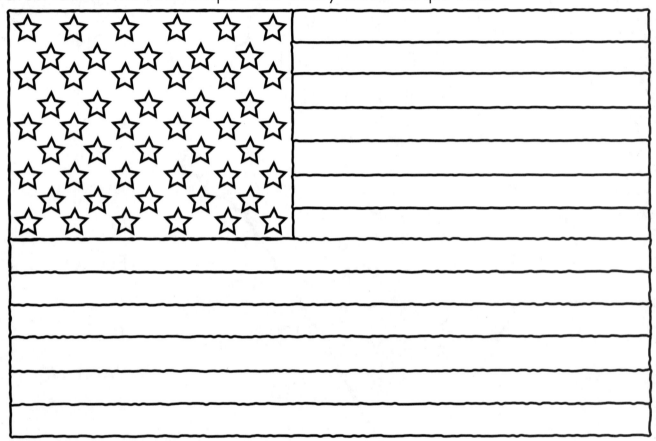

How many red stripes are on the flag? _____

How many white stripes are on the flag? _____

What do you think the color red stands for on the flag? _____

_____

What do you think the color white stand for on the flag? _____

_____

What do you think the color blue stands for on the flag? _____

_____

HP101

Happy Father's Day

Draw a cartoon showing the funniest thing your dad, grandpa, or uncle ever did. Write a caption for your cartoon.

Eating Healthy

List foods that belong in each group of the food pyramid.

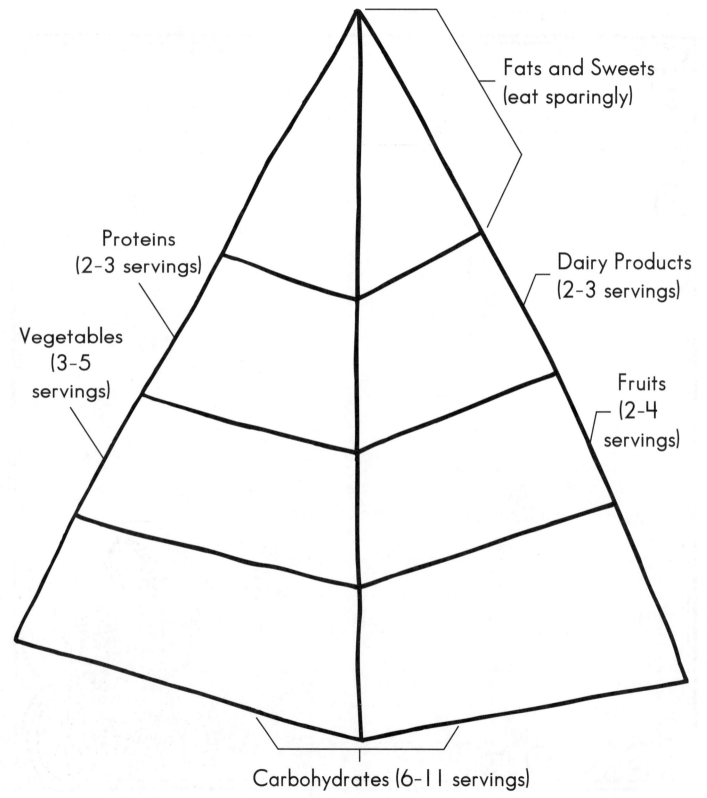

Fats and Sweets
(eat sparingly)

Proteins
(2-3 servings)

Dairy Products
(2-3 servings)

Vegetables
(3-5
servings)

Fruits
(2-4
servings)

Carbohydrates (6-11 servings)

Name _____ Date _____

Summer Safety

Use the code below to read this summer safety message. Write the letters in the blanks.

A	#	B	!	E	*	G	{ }	H	4	I	+
K	"	L	@	M	$	N	%	O	7	R	?
S	9	T	[ ]	U	3	W	=	Y	2		

__ __ __ __ __ __   __ __ __ __
\#   @   =   #   2   9   =   *   #   ?

__ __ __ __   __ __ __ __ __ __
2   7   3   ?   4   *   @ $ *   [ ]

__ __ __ __   __ __ __ __ __ __
=   4   *   %   !   +   "   +   %   { }

__ __ __ __ __ __ __ __ __ .
7   ?   9   "   #   [ ]   +   %   { }

Write why you think this is a good safety rule.

_____

_____

_____

_____

_____

Name _____ Date _____

Who Took the Vowels?

Summertime is sports time, but someone lost all the vowels from the names of these sports.

Fill in the blanks with A, E, I, O, or U to finish the words.

Circle your favorite sport.

1. G ____ L F

2. S ____ C C ____ R

3. H ____ C K ____ Y

4. T ____ N N ____ S

5. B ____ S K ____ T B ____ L L

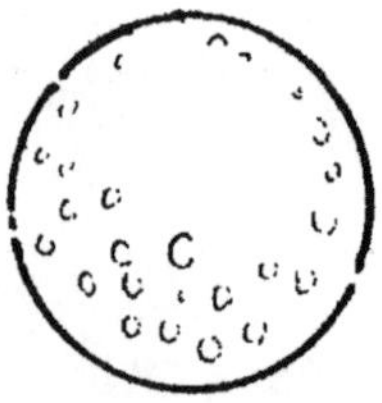

6. F ____ ____ T B ____ L L

7. S K ____ ____ N G

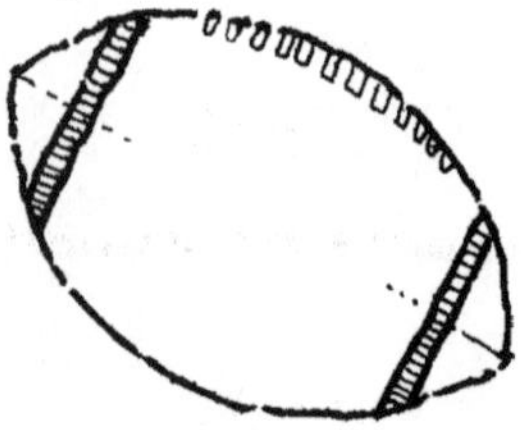

8. S K ____ T ____ N G

9. B ____ W L ____ N G

10. S W ____ M M ____ N G

HP101

Name _____   Date _____

⚾ Summer Words

Rewrite each group of words in A, B, C order.

_____ soccer		_____ May
_____ tennis		_____ June
_____ swimming		_____ July
_____ baseball		_____ August
_____		_____
_____ bat		_____ swings
_____ mitt		_____ slides
_____ bike		_____ play
_____ skateboard		_____ park
_____		_____
_____ ice cream		_____ read
_____ hot dogs		_____ hike
_____ hamburgers		_____ sing
_____ picnic		_____ march
_____		_____
_____ music		_____ circus
_____ march		_____ bears
_____ parade		_____ lions
_____ July		_____ tiger

HP101

Twenty Ways to Add to Twenty

There are many ways to add up to twenty.

Here are three ways: $20 + 0 = 20$

$19 + 1 = 20$

$18 + 1 + 1 = 20$

Fill in the seashells with 20 other ways to make 20.

Name _____   Date _____

Tell Me a Tale

Write a summer story. Use as many of the words in the box as you can in your story.

flower	green	sunny	stream
happy	cloudy	rainbow	garden
swim	jump	park	picnic
beach	vacation	play	children

_____

_____

_____

_____

_____

_____

_____

_____

_____

_____

_____

_____

HP101

Time for fun

Draw the hands on the clocks to show the correct times.

1. Aaron and Tori went to the beach on Monday at 9:30 A.M.

2. They stayed until 1:30 P.M.

3. On Tuesday, Cassie went shopping with her mother for new sandals. They left at 10:15 A.M.

4. Tobias and Rachel met Tori for lunch at 12:30 P.M.

5. Devan went to the baseball game with his Uncle Jay on Wednesday. The game started at 6:30 P.M.

6. The game went into extra innings and didn't finish until 11:10 P.M.

7. On Thursday, Maysie went to the zoo at 8:45 A.M.

8. She fed the seals at 9:20 A.M.

9. She watched the zookeeper feed the lions at 2:15 P.M.

10. Friday's soccer game started at 1:30 P.M.

11. After the game, everyone went for pizza at 4:50 P.M.

JULY/AUGUST

Help the Hikers (Answers)

1. 129; 2. 23; 3. 140; 4. 145; 5. 192; 6. 8; 7. 266;
8. 101 and 111

Fly the Flag on the Fourth of July (Solution)

F	L	A	G	O	P	R	R	P	R	P
I	A	B	C	D	E	F	N	R	H	A
R	I	J	K	L	M	N	O	U	O	R
E	P	Q	C	I	R	C	U	S	U	A
W	G	P	O	M	B	E	D	D	A	D
O	F	O	U	R	T	H	L	R	R	E
R	L	M	N	A	M	P	T	W	T	Z
K	P	O	T	E	F	U	N	N	W	N
S	H	O	R	E	A	L	L	U	S	U
J	U	L	Y	E	M	S	S	W	W	W
Z	Y	X	W	P	I	C	N	I	C	C
J	U	Y	L	P	L	P	Y	N	U	B
J	U	N	L	P	Y	Y	E	U	B	

Summer Insects (Activity)

Talk with children about different types of insects. Remind them that spiders, worms, and scorpions are not insects because they do not have six legs. Talk about why we see more insects in summer than in winter (especially in areas where winters include freezing temperatures). Go on an insect hunt together to see how many different types of insects you can spot.

Lions and Tigers and Bears: Oh, My! (Activity Extension)

Celebrate the July 5 birthday of P.T. Barnum, the showman who created "The Greatest Show on Earth." Encourage children to set up their own Circus Day complete with circus acts (none too dangerous), clowns, circus animals (pets and/or stuffed animals), decorations, and food.

Playing for Prizes (Answers)

bear $2.50; dog $7.50; elephant $3.75; tiger $8.00

Circus Day (Activity)

If children have never been to a real circus, this is the year to treat them—and yourself—to a great adventure.

Nouns from A to Z (Activity Extension)

If children are ready, explain the difference between common nouns and proper nouns. Remind them that all proper nouns begin with a capital letter. Run a second copy of this page. As a group, write several proper nouns for each letter of the alphabet.

Riddle Me (Answers)

1. He needed a "hop"-eration.; 2. "Here kitty, kitty.";
3. Bats; 4. Odor in the court!; 5. Whatever the ant eats.; 6. Take the tooth ferry.; 7. A box of quackers;
8. A quack; 9. Get up a half hour later.

Riddle Me (Activity Extension)

Encourage children to make up their own riddles and share them with the group.

Let children select their favorite riddles and illustrate them.

Picnic Time (Activity)

Picnics are fun on the Fourth of July and on any nice day in summer at a favorite park or beach. If you don't want to travel, picnic in your backyard, on your porch or patio. Plan a no-cook menu children can help prepare like meat and cheese sandwiches, fresh fruit, raw veggies, cookies, and lemonade.

Summer Words (Activity)

Ask children to brainstorm for "summer words." Write their words on chart paper and read the list together when you finish.

July Is National Ice Cream Month (Activity)

Celebrate National Ice Cream Month with a double dip of your favorite flavor. Be adventurous. Try some new flavors you've never tasted.

Invite children to make up and name their own new flavor of ice cream. Let the other children vote on whether they'd try it. Not too many would be willing to try spinach and liver flavored ice cream, but something called polka-dot surprise might appeal.

Help the Hikers

Rabbit and Turtle plan to hike during July and August. Help them decide where to go by solving the math equations on each sign! The answers will show how many miles to each place.

Miles to
Violet Valley

$$\begin{array}{r} 55 \\ + 74 \\ \hline \end{array}$$

1.

Miles to
Possum Peak

$105 - 82 =$

2.

Miles to
Crooked Creek

$$\begin{array}{r} 97 \\ + 43 \\ \hline \end{array}$$

3.

Miles to
Raccoon
Ridge

$$\begin{array}{r} 215 \\ - 60 \\ \hline \end{array}$$

4.

Miles to
Mighty Mountain

$79 + 113 =$

5.

Miles to
Wilderness Woods

$$\begin{array}{r} 22 \\ - 14 \\ \hline \end{array}$$

6.

Miles to
Greenland
Gully

$$\begin{array}{r} 116 \\ + 150 \\ \hline \end{array}$$

7.

Miles to
Lily Lake

$$\begin{array}{r} 200 \\ - 99 \\ \hline \end{array}$$

$$\begin{array}{r} \\ + 10 \\ \hline \end{array}$$

8.

Fly the Flag on the Fourth of July

Find the words hidden in the flag.

F	L	A	G	O	P	R	P	R	P
I	A	B	C	D	E	F	R	H	A
R	I	J	K	L	M	N	O	U	R
E	P	Q	C	I	R	C	U	S	A
W	G	P	O	M	B	E	D	A	D
O	F	O	U	R	T	H	L	R	E
R	L	M	N	A	M	P	T	W	Z
K	P	O	T	E	F	U	N	N	N
S	H	O	R	E	A	L	L	U	U
J	U	L	Y	E	M	S	S	W	W
Z	Y	X	W	P	I	C	N	I	C
J	U	Y	L	P	L	Y	N	U	B
J	U	N	L	P	Y	Y	E	U	B

circus	country	family	flag
fireworks	fourth	fun	July
parade	picnic	proud	USA

Our flag is a symbol of our country. The 13 stripes stand for the first 13 colonies. The 50 stars stand for the 50 states.

Draw a symbol that would be good for your family.

Playing for Prizes

Vince played games all day at the Fourth of July carnival. He won lots of cool prizes! Add the amounts in each column to find out what he spent to win the prizes at the bottom. Write the totals on the stuffed animals.

50¢	$1.50	75¢	$2.00
50¢	$1.50	75¢	$2.00
50¢	$1.50	75¢	$2.00
50¢	$1.50	75¢	$2.00
50¢	$1.50	75¢	$2.00

HP101

Circus Day

It's time for the circus to begin, but where are the clowns? Where are the animals, the jugglers, and the acrobats? Finish the circus picture and color it.

Name _____ Date _____

Lions and Tigers and Bears: Oh, My!

Draw in the missing parts for these animals. Then color the picture.

HP101

Name _____   Date _____

Nouns from A to Z

A noun is the name of a person, place, or thing. **Girl**, **city**, and **candy** are nouns. Write nouns that begin with each letter of the alphabet.

A _____   _____

B _____   _____

C _____   _____

D _____   _____

E _____   _____

F _____   _____

G _____   _____

H _____   _____

I _____   _____

J _____   _____

K _____   _____

L _____   _____

M _____   _____

N _____   _____

O _____   _____

P _____   _____

Q _____   _____

R _____   _____

S _____   _____

T _____   _____

U _____   _____

V _____   _____

W _____   _____

X _____   _____

Y _____   _____

Z _____   _____

HP101

Name _____ Date _____

Summer Insects

We see many insects in summer. All insects have six legs and three body parts.

This is a Mayfly.   This is called a June bug.

Draw insects for July and August and name them.

July Insect Name: _____

August Insect Name: _____

HP101

Color the Catch

Todd loves to fish! Look what he brought back to the cabin! Read the instructions, then color his catch accordingly.

If the number is . . .

> 50 color it red.

< 50 color it yellow.

If the number is . . .

> 100 color it blue.

< 100 color it green.

HP101

Riddle Me

It's summer vacation! Relax.
Giggle. Share a riddle.

1. Why did the frog go to the hospital?

2. What does a 1,000 pound mouse say to a cat?

3. What animals attend every baseball game?

4. What did the judge shout when the skunk entered the classroom?

5. What is smaller than an ant's mouth?

6. How do you get to a dentist who lives on an island?

7. What do you get when you put ten ducks in a box?

8. What kind of doctor would a duck be?

9. What should you do if you feel dizzy for the first thirty minutes every day when you get up?

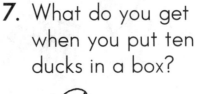

HP101